The PARENTS' GUIDE to PUBERTY

The PARENTS' GUIDE to PUBERTY

Helping your child to thrive
(not just survive) as they grow up

Gath Hakanson

The Parents' Guide to Puberty
Helping your child to thrive (not just survive) as they grow up
By Cath Hakanson

Published by Sex Ed Rescue
PO Box 7903
Cloisters Square WA 6000
Australia

sexedrescue.com

Cover artwork by Claire Cassidy from Studio Flos
Illustrations by Elettra Codignotto

For permission contact:
cath@sexedrescue.com

ISBN-13: 978-0-6487162-5-9

CONTENTS

INTRODUCTION

You're already an expert on puberty because you've been through it yourself.

Maybe you've noticed that your child is moodier lately or starting to grow hair in new places. Maybe they aren't showing any signs themself, but you've noticed changes in their friends.

Whichever it is, deep down, you realize that it's time to have the talk that you probably never had, or had too late, when you were growing up. It's time to prepare your child for what's to come.

If you're like most parents, including me, preparing your child for puberty probably isn't something you've ever thought about before. And now you realize how unprepared you are to talk about it. Well, you can relax for a moment, because this book will prepare you for what lies ahead. It will tell you everything you need to know before you talk to your child about the changes that will take place in them. This book covers important things such as what puberty is all about, why it happens, when and how you should start talking, and what you should talk about.

For more than 25 years, I've been helping people get more comfortable with sex. I've answered their questions, listened to their fears, empowered them with the right information, and pointed them in the right direction. After hearing thousands of parents ask me the same questions about puberty over and over again, I've worked out what they want.

Parents want to know how to have honest conversations that will guide their child through puberty and strengthen their relationship without them feeling embarrassed, awkward or nervous.

But they don't know how to start.

This book will help you get started with talking. It will help you to:

- Understand what puberty means for your child so you are fully prepared to answer their questions.
- Realize the importance of discussing puberty before it starts so your child isn't surprised, confused or frightened.
- Know the evolving changes that happen during puberty, and when they are likely to happen, so you can confidently identify them and prepare your child for what comes next.
- Create crucial talking points you can use with your child before they get misinformation from somewhere else, so you know the right information to share at the right time.
- Develop basic tools to help you easily talk to your child, even if they are reluctant to talk about puberty.
- Provide you with age-appropriate answers to your child's questions, so that you are never at a loss for words.

Throughout this book, you will notice that I use slightly different language when talking about 'boys' and 'girls.' Instead of saying 'boys,' I will say 'male,' 'someone with a male body' or 'someone with a penis.' Instead of saying 'girls,' I will say 'female,' 'someone with a female body' or 'someone with a vagina.' This is because not everyone identifies with the gender they were raised as.

This book won't just show you how to talk to your child about puberty. It will show you how to have the type of relationship where they can talk to you about anything, no matter what. But you need to start talking sooner rather than later, because puberty is on its way, whether you like it or not!

As much as we would all like to leave it for someone else to address (me included), you love your child and know they deserve to hear about the changes that are going to happen to them from you, so that they can turn to you for support, guidance and information.

Empower your child with the right information so that when the time comes, they don't make the wrong decisions around love, sex and relationships.

All the best!

Cath

You can access my FREE sex education course for parents at https://sexedrescue.com/back-to-basics/

WHAT IS PUBERTY?

Puberty is going to happen whether you want it to or not but at least it happens gradually.

Puberty can mean many different things, but basically, it is when your child's body changes from being a child to an adult. It is the last time that their body will grow. Puberty isn't the last time that their body will change, though, because, as we know, our bodies will keep on changing for our whole lives. Luckily, puberty doesn't happen overnight. It can take from two-to-five and up to 10 years for your child's body to change. This is a good thing, as it gives them time to get used to the changes that will slowly be happening to them. Puberty is about more than just their body changing. Their relationships with their family, friends and peers will change. Their feelings and even their personality will change, too.

What does this all mean?

Puberty means your child will soon be fertile, that they can make a baby. And that you could become a grandparent! But does this mean that they are ready to become a parent? Most likely not. Just because their body is capable of reproducing doesn't mean they're necessarily ready to become a parent, but they do need to know that this could happen.

When will puberty happen?

The time puberty starts is different for everyone. It can be earlier for some kids and later for others. Everyone is different.

For children with a vagina, puberty will start any time between the ages of eight and 15. And for children with a penis, puberty will usually start a year later, between the ages of nine and 15.

When your child's body is the right size and shape for them, the hormones that start the changes will be triggered and their body will begin to change. It is important to remember that you can't rush or delay puberty. This can be hard for some kids, especially if they're the first or the last to show changes. They will see themselves as being different from their friends and will wonder if they are normal.

If they're an early bloomer, your child will probably attract unwanted attention from their peers and be teased about having breasts, being smelly or gaining weight. They will most likely be wondering what's wrong with them, as they are the only one whose body is changing. If they're a late bloomer, they may be worried that they haven't yet started to change, and they will wonder what is wrong with them. It is important that your child understands that puberty will happen when their body is ready for it, and that everybody is different.

If you started puberty early (or late), then there's a good chance that your child will start puberty sooner (or later) too.

When to worry

Some kids start puberty earlier or later than you would expect. An early start to puberty is called precocious puberty.

Precocious puberty is a lot more common in children born with a vagina than with a penis.

For children born with a vagina, precocious puberty is defined as the development of breasts before the age of eight, or the start of periods before the age of nine. If this happens to your child, you should seek medical advice.

If your child does not have any physical signs of puberty by the age of 15 to 16, or periods by the age of 16 to 17, you should seek medical advice as to why puberty is delayed. Usually, puberty is delayed because of a hormonal imbalance, being underweight, or being under extreme stress. Rarely, developmental or chromosomal abnormalities can be found.

For children born with a penis, precocious puberty is when, before the age of nine, they show signs of:

- Growth of the testicles and penis
- Growth of pubic, underarm or facial hair
- Rapid height growth, i.e., a growth spurt
- Voice deepening
- Acne
- Adult body odor

If any of this happens to your child before the age of nine, you should seek medical advice. If they don't have any physical signs of puberty by the age of 14, you should seek medical advice regarding why puberty is delayed. For most children with a penis, puberty may be late because it was also late in one or both parents. It could also be delayed because of a hormonal imbalance, being underweight, or being under extreme stress. Rarely, developmental or chromosomal abnormalities can be found.

What makes puberty happen?

Hormones are responsible for making the changes to your child's body during puberty. Hormones are chemicals that all our bodies make. They travel throughout the body in our bloodstream, from the place they are made, to the place they do their work. Their job is to start something working. During puberty, the job of some hormones is to make the body capable of reproducing.

So, let's look at how puberty happens in a female and male body. Despite the differences, there are some similarities.

What happens to kids born with a female body?

The pituitary gland

During puberty, it all starts because of a gland at the base of the brain known as the pituitary gland. One day, when the body is ready, the brain sends a message to the pituitary gland that tells it to start releasing growth hormones into the bloodstream. The hypothalamus produces a hormone called gonadotrophin-releasing hormone (GnRH). This hormone stimulates the pituitary gland to release two hormones: follicle-stimulating hormone (FSH) and luteinizing hormone (LH). These hormones travel through the blood to the ovaries and trigger the release of estrogen and progesterone.

THE PITUITARY GLAND

The pituitary gland sends a message to the ovaries, telling them to start making estrogen and progesterone.

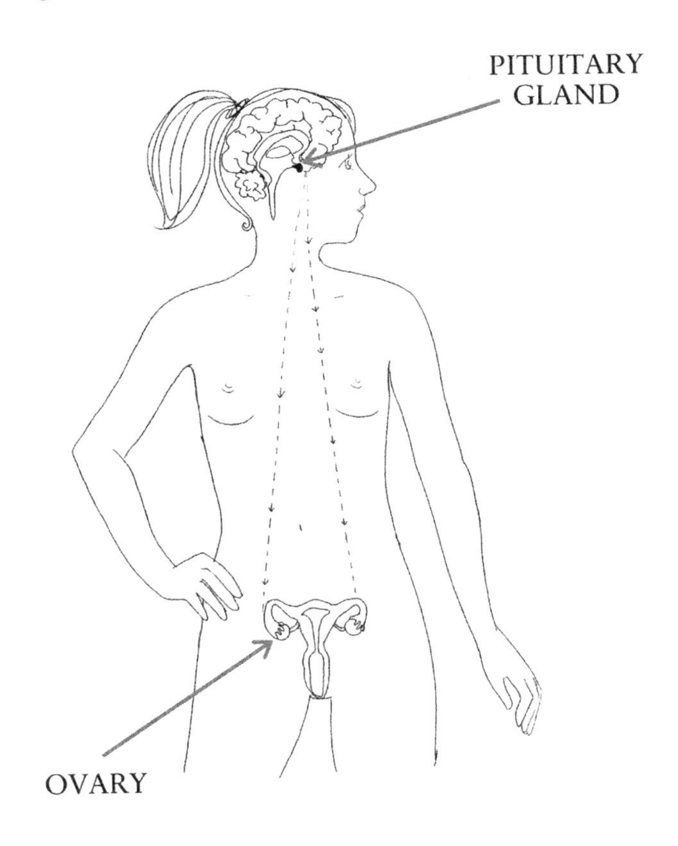

The pituitary gland is the master gland that tells all other glands what to do. It tells the other glands to start making the hormones that are needed to turn your child into an adult. Hormones are the chemical messages that allow different parts of the body to communicate with each other. Think of it like a telephone line, where everyone's telephones are connected by wire cables, and we can send messages (talk) through the telephone lines. The body has its own telephone lines (bloodstream), where the glands are sending hormones (chemical messages) to the different parts of the body. The pituitary gland sends a message to the ovaries, telling them to start producing the hormones progesterone and estrogen. This causes the egg (ovum) to be released from the ovary.

Estrogen and Progesterone

These important hormones have different jobs to do. Estrogen is responsible for the growth of breasts, the changes in body shape such as hips, legs, and breasts, and the development of the reproductive organs. Progesterone and estrogen together prepare the uterus for menstruation or pregnancy.

Ovulation

Your child's eggs have been inside their ovaries since they were a fetus growing inside a uterus. Estrogen tells the eggs to mature. It also tells the ovaries to prepare an egg (ovum) for release into the fallopian tubes. The egg will travel along the fallopian tubes and into the uterus. This whole process of ripening an egg for release from the ovary is called ovulation. Ovulation is when the eggs stored in the ovaries begin to ripen, with one being released every four weeks or so, plus or minus a few days.

OVULATION

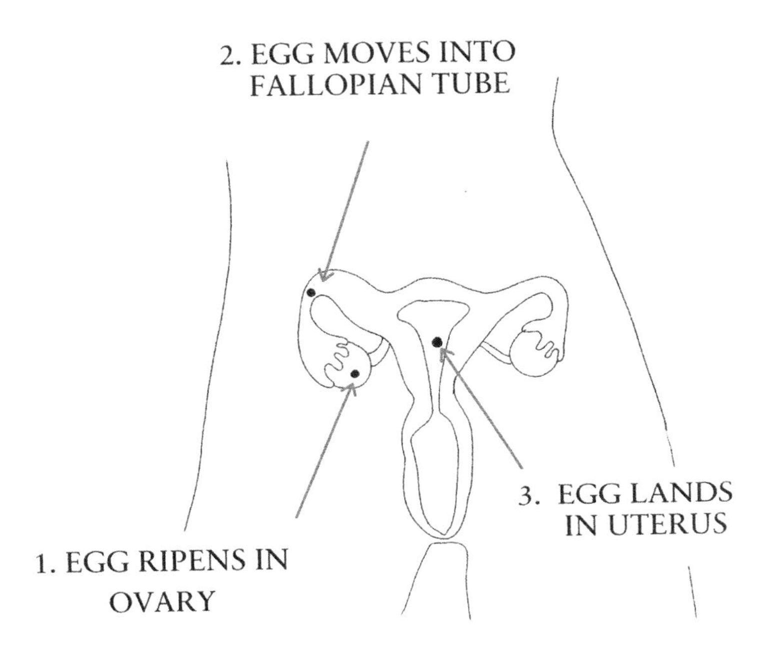

The ovaries are about the size of a large grape. An ovum (egg) is the size of a grain of sand. The uterus is about the size of a pear.

Menstruation

While the egg is ripening and getting ready to come out, the lining of the uterus starts to thicken, just in case a sperm joins with the egg, resulting in pregnancy. If the egg is joined with a sperm, the body will begin to prepare itself for pregnancy. If the egg is not joined with a sperm, the lining of the uterus will begin to dissolve. This dissolved lining comes out of the vagina and is known as a period, menstruation or menstrual blood. Two weeks after the period, another egg is released and the whole process of ovulation begins all over again.

MENSTRUATION

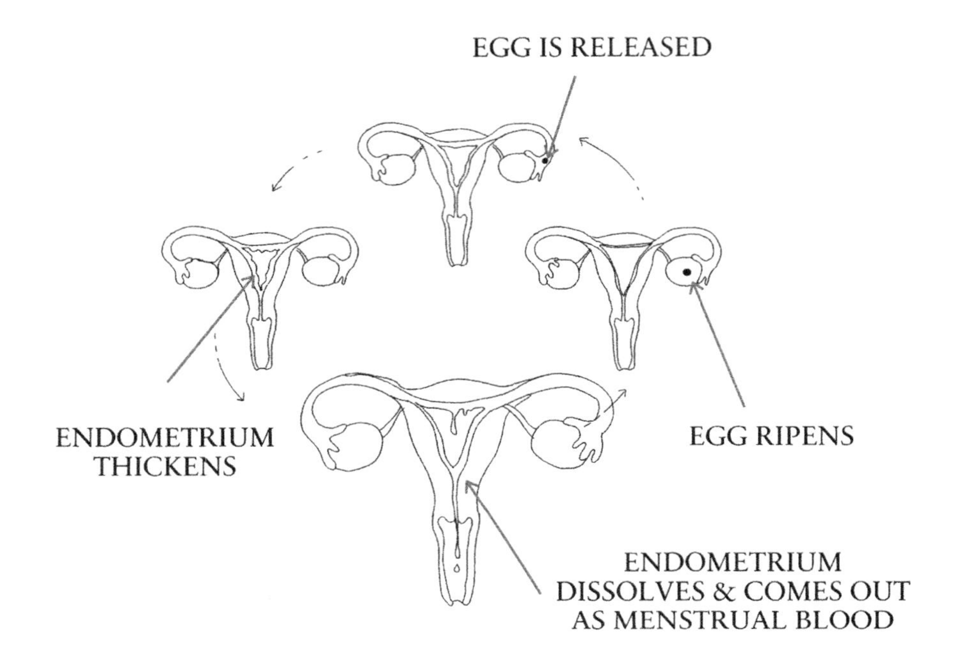

What happens to kids born with a male body?

The pituitary gland

During puberty, it all starts because of a gland at the base of the brain known as the pituitary gland. One day, when the body is ready, the brain sends a message to the pituitary gland that tells it to start releasing growth hormones into the bloodstream. The hypothalamus produces a hormone called gonadotrophin-releasing hormone (GnRH). This hormone stimulates the pituitary gland to release two hormones: follicle-stimulating hormone (FSH) and luteinizing hormone (LH). These hormones travel through the blood to the testicles (testes) to make the hormone testosterone and to get ready to make sperm.

THE PITUITARY GLAND

The pituitary gland sends a message to the testicles, telling them to start making testosterone and sperm.

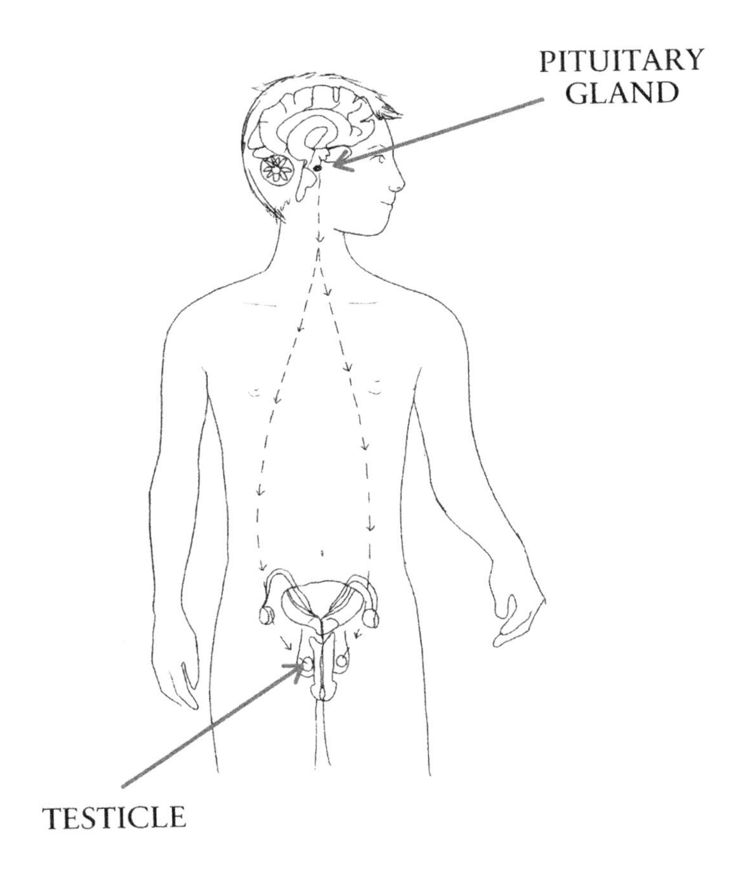

The pituitary gland is the master gland that tells all other glands what to do. It tells the other glands to start making the hormones that are needed to turn your child into an adult. Hormones are the chemical messages that allow different parts of the body to communicate with each other. Think of it like a telephone line, where everyone's telephones are connected by wire cables, and we can send messages (talk) through the telephone lines. The body has its own telephone lines (bloodstream), where the glands are sending hormones (chemical messages) to the different parts of the body.

Follicle-stimulating hormone

Follicle-stimulating hormone (FSH) has an important job to do. When FSH reaches the testicles, it spurs the growth of the seminiferous tubules, which is where sperm is made. Over a couple of years, the testicles will slowly grow bigger as all this new growth happens inside of them.

During puberty, the testicles will grow to about the size of a plum.

SEMINIFEROUS TUBULES

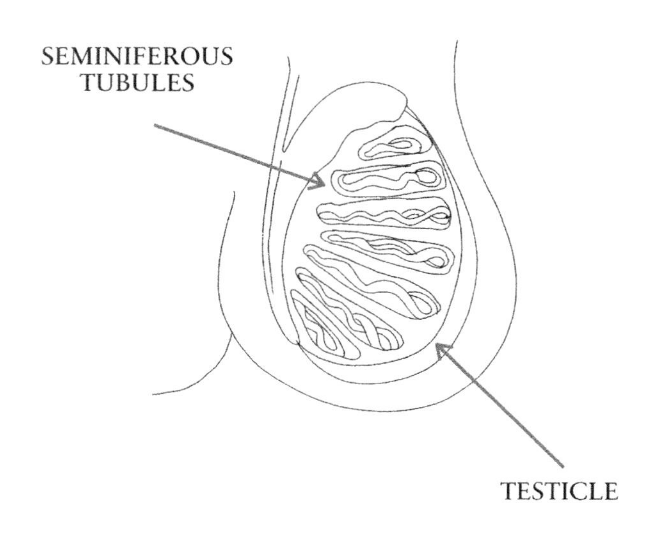

This can take a couple of years to happen. Once these tubules are fully grown, the body is then ready to start maturing the sperm to be ready for reproduction. This means that they will now be able to ejaculate and semen, which contains the sperm, will come out of their penis.

Luteinizing hormone

Luteinizing hormone (LH) has a different job to do. It triggers special cells inside the testes, called Leydig cells, to start producing hormones called androgens. The main androgen that the Leydig cells make is called testosterone. Girls have testosterone too, but not as much as boys. Androgens are hormones that tell the body that it's time to mature or grow up. It helps to make the male changes, things like a deeper voice, face/armpit/pubic hair, and the start of their sex drive.

Testosterone helps to get certain parts of the body, like the prostate gland and the seminal vesicles, ready to care for and carry the mature sperm. When everything is ready, testosterone will then tell the testicles that it is time to start maturing the sperm to be ready for reproduction via ejaculation. This means that they will now be able to ejaculate, and semen, which contains the sperm, will come out of their penis.

Sperm

Sperm or spermatozoa are the male reproductive cells. Sperm are a bit different than the reproductive cells that females have. Females are born with their ova or eggs, whereas males aren't born with their sperm. During puberty, the testicles will start to make sperm for the very first time. When all the reproductive organs are fully grown, your child's body will be capable of ejaculating. This means they are now fertile and will eventually be capable of creating a baby, if their sperm joins with an egg during sexual intercourse.

Technically speaking, though, your child won't be capable of producing enough sperm to fertilize an egg through sexual intercourse until after about six-to-18 months of ejaculating. But, to keep things simple, it is best to think of them as being fertile once they begin to ejaculate. You don't want to become a grandparent too soon!

Sperm are so tiny they can't be seen without a microscope.

SPERM

Erection

An erection is when the penis becomes stiff and hard, larger and longer, and stands out from the body. Erections happen to kids all the time – from when they are a fetus growing inside their mother's uterus and right through their childhood.

As they go through puberty, erections begin to happen more frequently and for a different reason. Now they start to happen so that the sperm can get to the ovum (egg) and fertilize it. For this to be happen, the penis needs to be erect so that it can be pushed into the vagina, where the sperm is delivered, and fertilization can happen.

Erections are all about an increased blood flow to the penis. The brain sends a chemical message to the blood vessels in the penis. The arteries relax and open to let more blood in. At the same time, the veins close, trapping the blood inside the penis. There is a lot of spongy tissue inside the penis. When it is filled with blood, that soft spongy tissue will go firm or hard, making the penis expand because of all the extra blood inside it. The penis will become larger, firmer, and stand out from the body. It is now erect. When the erection is over, the veins will relax, letting the extra blood back into the body. At the same time, the arteries will close, only letting a small amount of blood into the penis. The penis then becomes soft again.

ERECTION

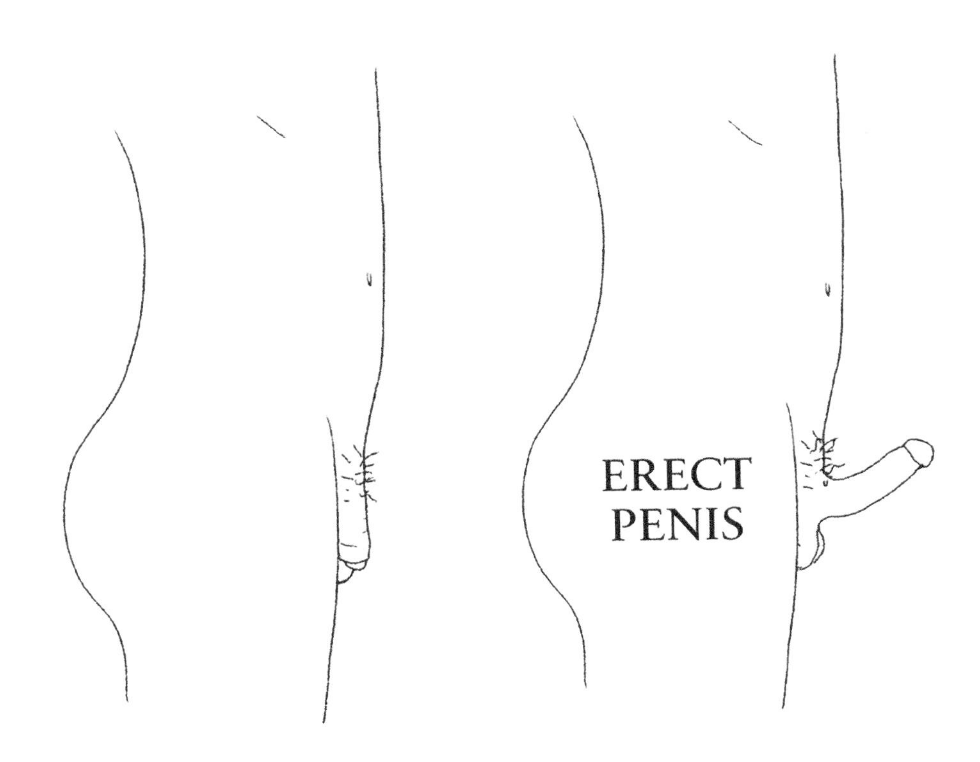

Ejaculation

Ejaculation is when sperm are suddenly released from the body. This can only happen when the penis is erect. It can happen during sexual intercourse, masturbation, or during a "wet dream" (also called nocturnal emission).

When the body is getting close to ejaculation, the sperm will begin their journey to leave the body. Sperm are made in the testicles. They then mature in coiled tubes attached to the top of each testicle – the epididymis. When the body is getting close to ejaculation, the mature sperm travel up into the body through some tubes called the vas deferens. On their way, they mix with different fluids from the seminal vesicles and the prostate gland. This mixture of sperm and fluid is now called semen. Its job is to nourish the sperm and to keep it healthy.

Semen is a creamy white fluid. It can contain millions of sperm, with up to 300-to-500 million sperm coming out at a time!

The semen then travels through a tube that runs down the center of the penis (urethra) and spurts out of the opening at the tip of the penis. Strong muscle contractions squeeze the semen out. An orgasm usually happens with ejaculation, but not always. Sometimes you can ejaculate without an orgasm. It is not easy to explain how an orgasm feels, because it can be different each time. You could describe it as a really nice feeling that starts in the genitals and can also be felt throughout the whole body. This feeling then begins to feel stronger and stronger, building up until you begin to feel waves of intense feelings. For people with a penis, these feelings usually reach their peak with ejaculation, when the sperm comes out of the penis, but not always. Sometimes you won't ejaculate with an orgasm. After ejaculation, the penis will become soft and slowly return to its normal size.

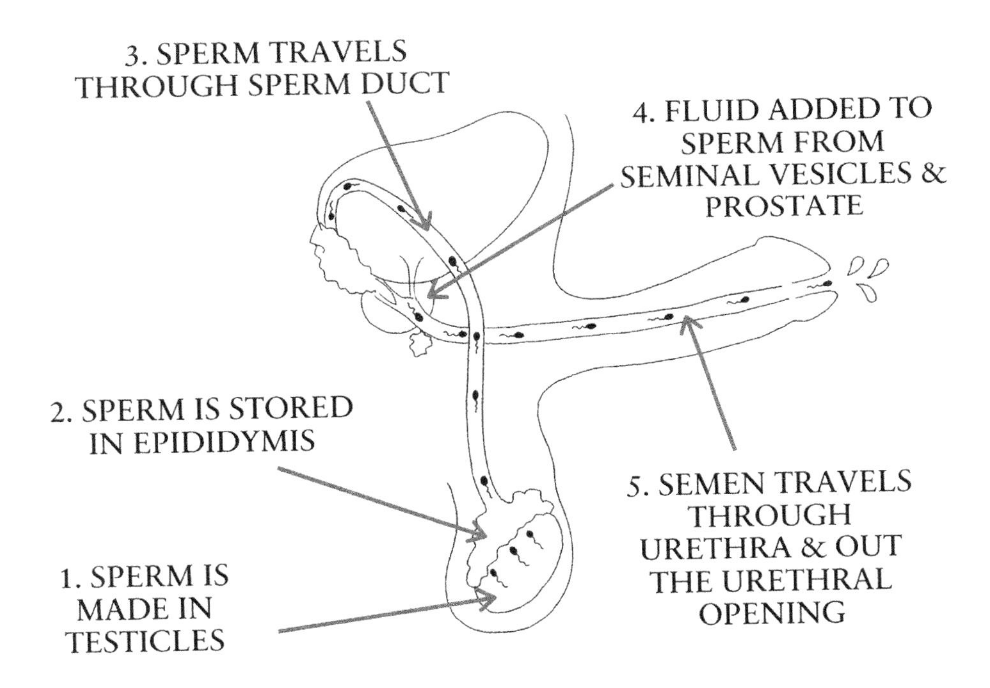

Fertilization

This is what happens when the sperm meets the egg. Fertilization usually happens during sexual intercourse, but it can also happen with assistance, for example, with in vitro fertilization (IVF). During sexual intercourse, sperm is released into the vagina when the penis ejaculates semen. The sperm will then swim through the vagina and uterus and up into the fallopian tubes, looking for an egg to fertilize. The egg is fertilized while it is still within the fallopian tube. It will continue travelling along the fallopian tube and into the uterus, where it will attach itself to the thickened uterine lining.

FERTILIZATION

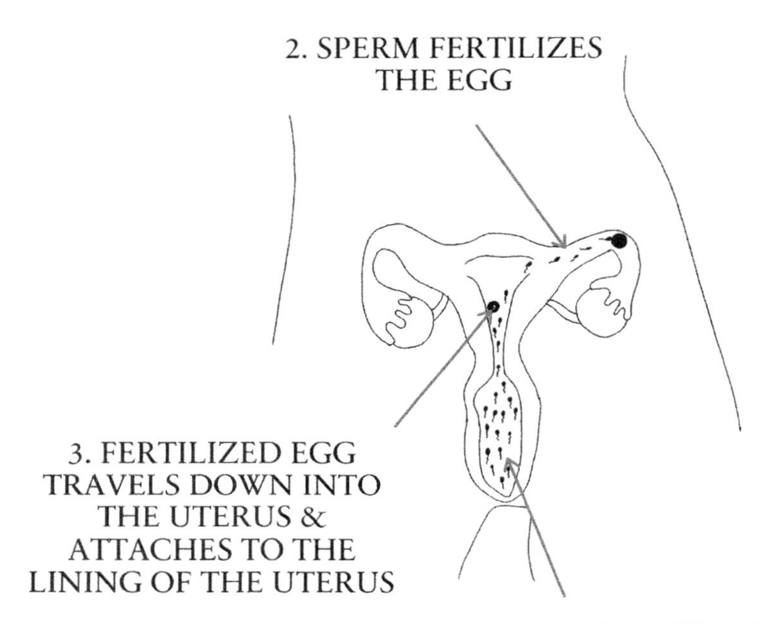

The body parts

When you start talking about puberty, it is important to know the names of the different parts you will be talking about. Below you will find some images and child-friendly definitions your child will understand.

If you are unsure about how to say any of these words, use an online dictionary for the pronunciation.

Before you use these words with your child, first practice saying them aloud to yourself. Talking about puberty and sex can be stressful enough without the added worry of trying to remember how to pronounce the words correctly!

Sexual anatomy for people with a vagina

Anus: The opening that is below the vulva, where feces (poo) comes out. Males have an anus too.

Bladder: A stretchy bag that holds the urine (pee) before it comes out of the body. The urine leaves the bladder through a small tube called the urethra. Males have a bladder too.

Cervix: The opening of the uterus that joins it with the vagina. You can find it deep inside, at the very top of your vagina.

Clitoris: A part that is behind the vulva and wraps around the vagina. The smallest part, about the size of a pea, can be seen outside the body, hidden under a small bump of skin, just above the urethra where the pee comes out. It can feel good when you touch it.

Fallopian tubes: Special tubes, like cooked spaghetti, that carry the egg from the ovaries to the uterus.

Labia majora: The outer lips that surround the vaginal opening. These are thicker and will eventually be covered in hair on the outside skin.

Labia minora: The inner lips that surround the vaginal opening. These are thinner and will not be covered in hair.

Mons pubis: The soft rounded area that sits above the pubic bone. Eventually, it will be covered in pubic hair.

Ovaries: Special organs that produce the eggs or ova. They are about the size of a grape.

Rectum: A tube that is used to store feces (poo) before it is pushed out through the anus. Males have a rectum too.

Uterus: A bag made of muscle that is about the size of a pear. It is the place for a baby to grow and stretches bigger as the baby grows.

Urethra: A narrow tube that leaves from the bladder and comes out of a small opening in the vulva.

Urethral opening: The small opening in the vulva where the urethra comes out of the body. It can be found between the clitoris and the vagina. Males have a urethral opening too.

Vagina: A stretchy tube that goes from the uterus to the outside of the body. It is the opening that you can feel at the bottom of the vulva.

Vulva: Thick folds of skin that cover the opening to the vagina. There is an outer part, which is the labia majora, and an inner part, which is the labia minora.

FEMALE INTERNAL (FRONT VIEW)

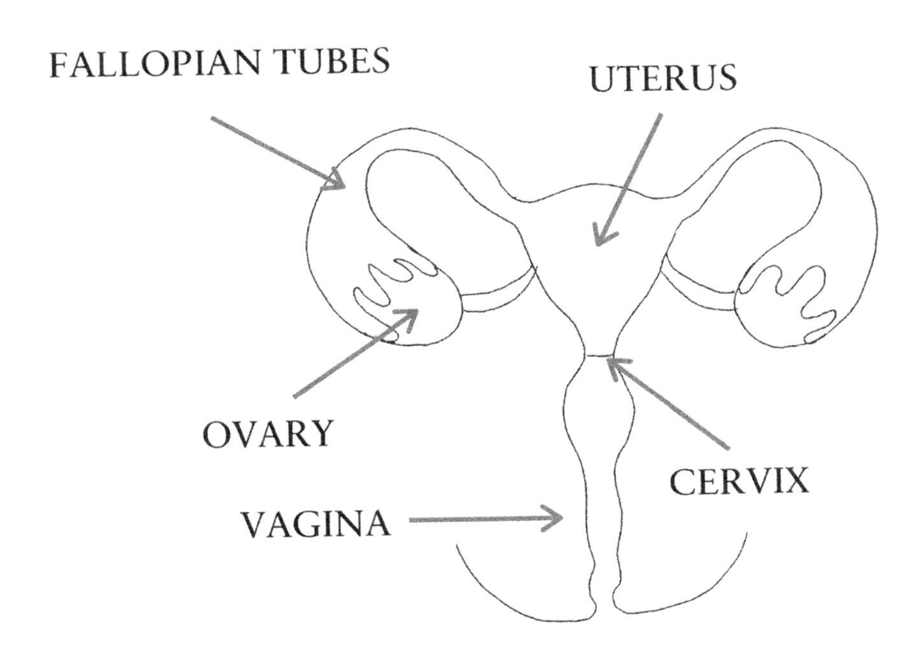

FEMALE INTERNAL (SIDE VIEW)

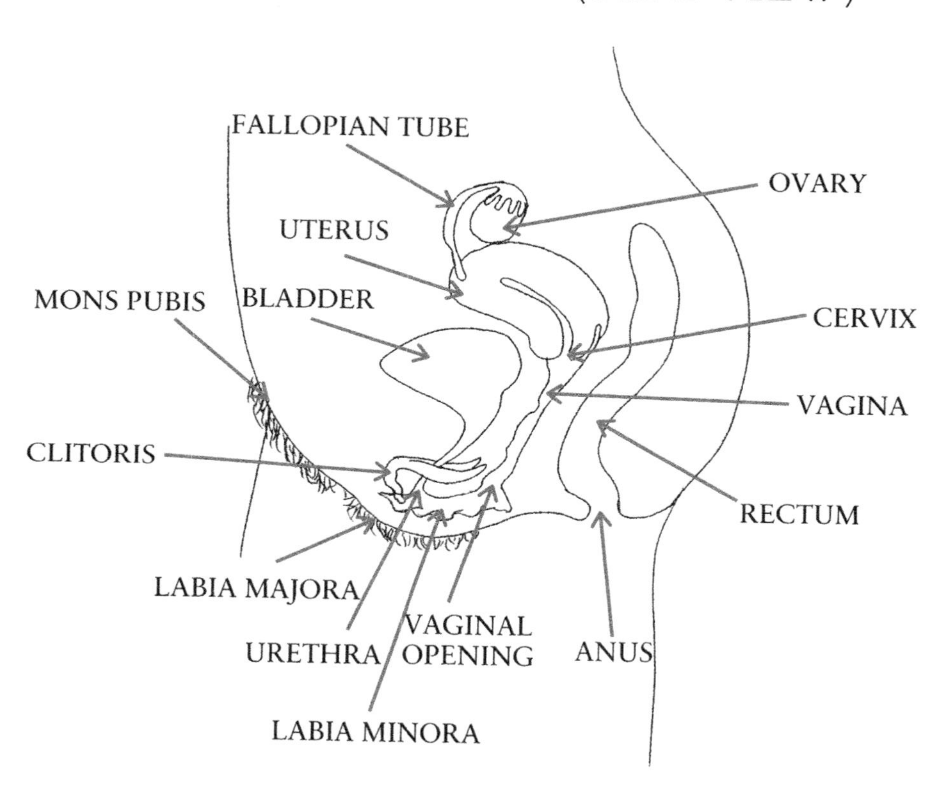

FEMALE EXTERNAL

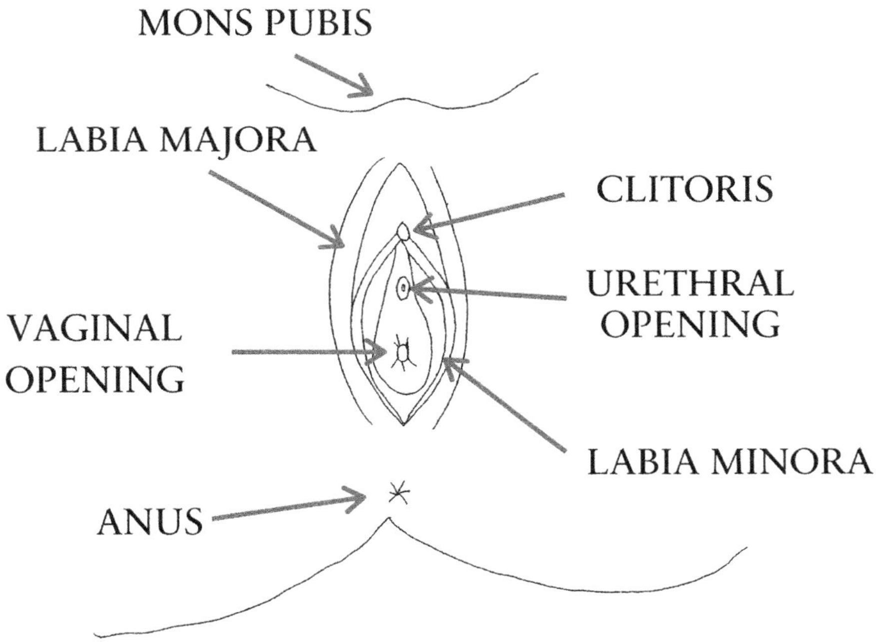

MONS PUBIS

LABIA MAJORA

CLITORIS

URETHRAL OPENING

VAGINAL OPENING

LABIA MINORA

ANUS

THE CLITORIS

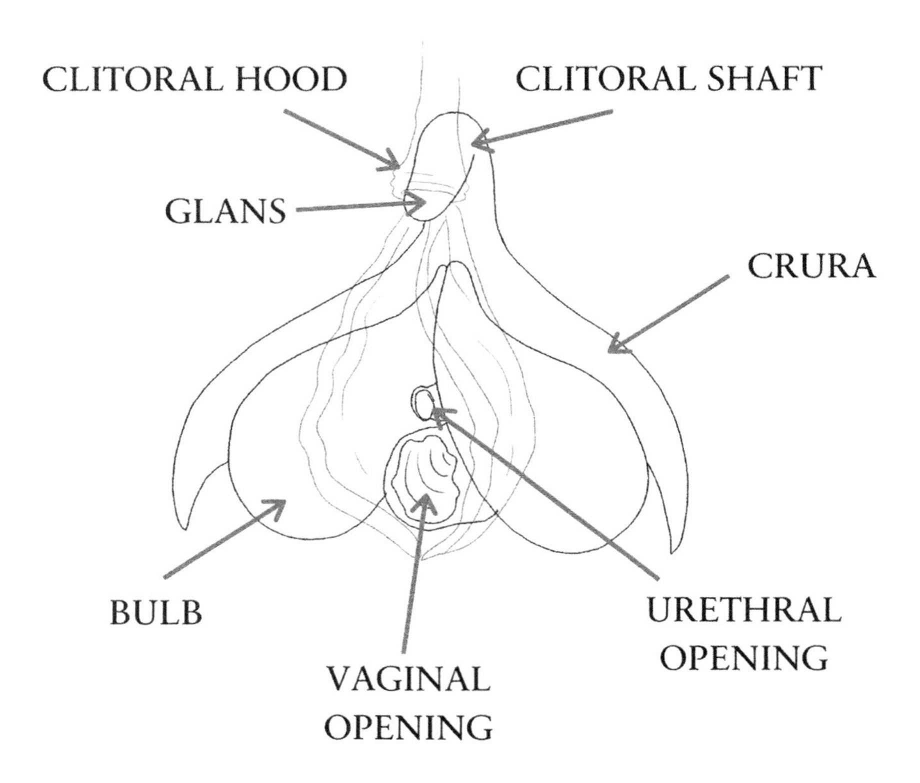

Sexual anatomy for people with a penis

Anus: The opening that is behind the scrotum, where feces (poo) comes out. Females have an anus too.

Bladder: A stretchy bag that holds the urine (pee) before it comes out of the body. The urine leaves the bladder through a small tube called the urethra. Females have a bladder too.

Corona: The ridge that runs around the bottom of the glans, where it joins the body of the penis.

Cowper's gland: These two small, round glands (the size of a pea) are found underneath the prostate gland. When a male starts to feel sexually aroused, they will start to make a special fluid that will lubricate the penis and keep the sperm safe as it travels through the urethra. The other name for this part is the bulbourethral gland.

Epididymis: The testicle is connected to the epididymis. Once sperm has been made in the testicles, it is sent to the epididymis. It is here that the sperm is grown up or matured, ready for reproduction. If felt through the scrotum, it will feel soft and squishy, like a piece of cooked spiral pasta.

Foreskin: The loose skin at the end of the penis. It protects the end of the penis, the glans, which is very sensitive to touch.

Frenulum: A sensitive piece of skin on the underside of the penis where the foreskin attaches itself to the glans. It helps the foreskin to contract or shrink itself over the glans and can only be seen when the foreskin is fully retracted.

Glans: The head or the tip of the penis. It has many nerve endings, which means it is sensitive to touch. In uncircumcised penises, this will be covered by the foreskin.

Penis: The part that hangs in front of the scrotum and sticks out. Urine comes out of the small opening at the end of it. The penis is also used for sexual intercourse, where it becomes erect, and semen comes out of the end of it, through the urethral opening.

Prostate gland: A gland that is at the base of the penis, near the bladder. The urethra runs through the center of it. The prostate gland helps with bladder control and secretes fluids that mix with the sperm to make semen.

Scrotum: The soft bag of squishy skin between the legs that holds and protects the testicles. It has a muscle that makes it expand with heat (e.g., when having a warm bath) and shrink with cold (e.g., when swimming in the ocean). This keeps the testicles at the right temperature to protect the sperm.

Seminal vesicles: A pair of glands that lie on either side of the bladder. They open into the vas deferens and secrete fluids that mix with the sperm to make semen.

Shaft: The length or body of the penis.

Testicles: The male sex organs that make sperm. They are two soft oval shaped parts that will grow much bigger during puberty, to about the size of a plum. Sperm is made in the testicles. If felt through the scrotum, a testicle will feel like a hard-boiled egg that has been peeled.

Urethra: A narrow tube that leaves from the bladder and goes through the penis to the small opening at the tip of the penis (urethral opening). It also carries the semen after it leaves the vas deferens.

Urethral opening: The slit at the end of the penis (through the glans) where urine and semen come out. Females have a urethral opening too.

Vas deferens: The tube that connects the testicles/epididymis to the prostate and seminal vesicles. If felt through the scrotum, it will feel like a piece of cooked spaghetti.

MALE INTERNAL (FRONT VIEW)

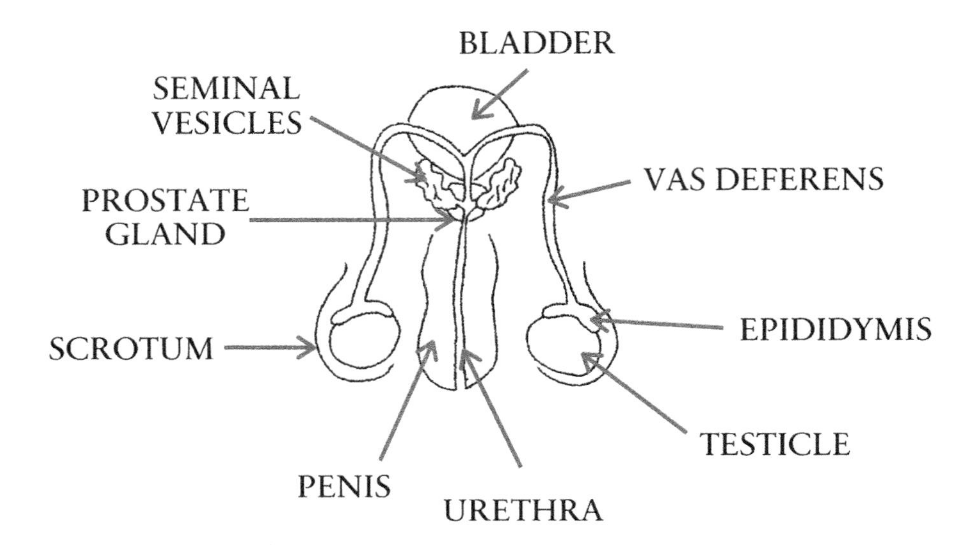

MALE INTERNAL (SIDE VIEW)

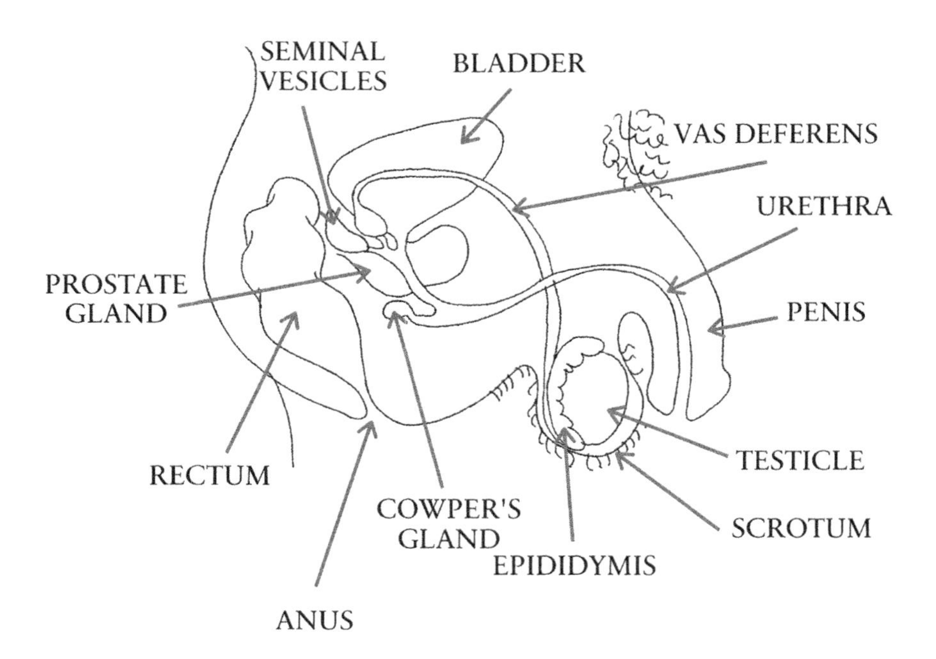

MALE EXTERNAL (CIRCUMCISED)

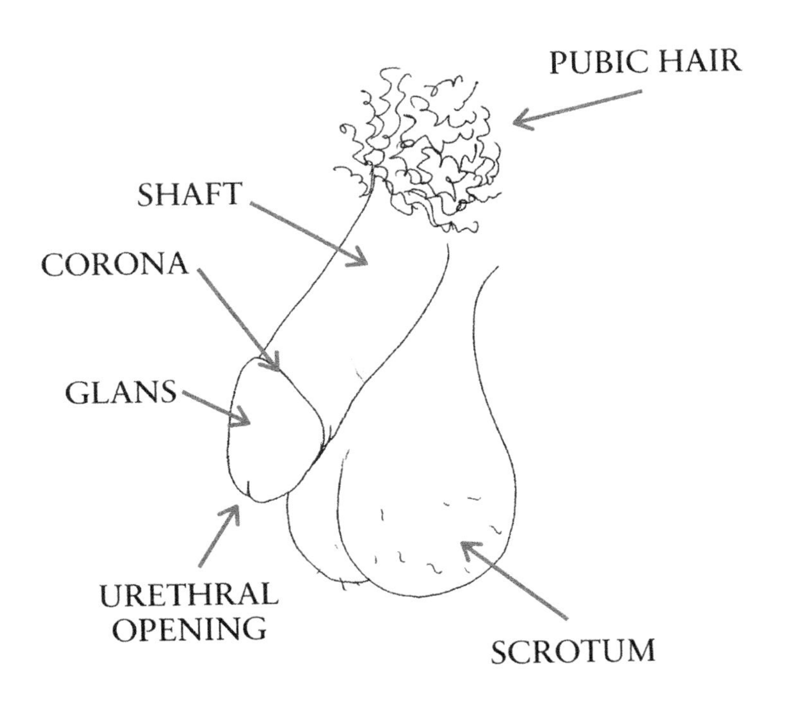

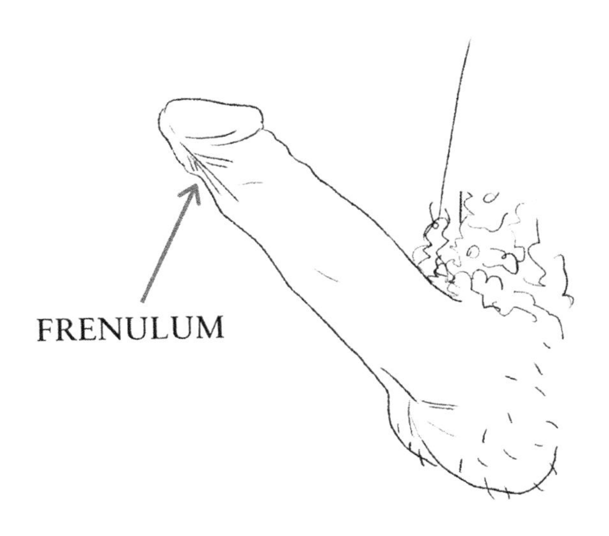

MALE EXTERNAL (INTACT)

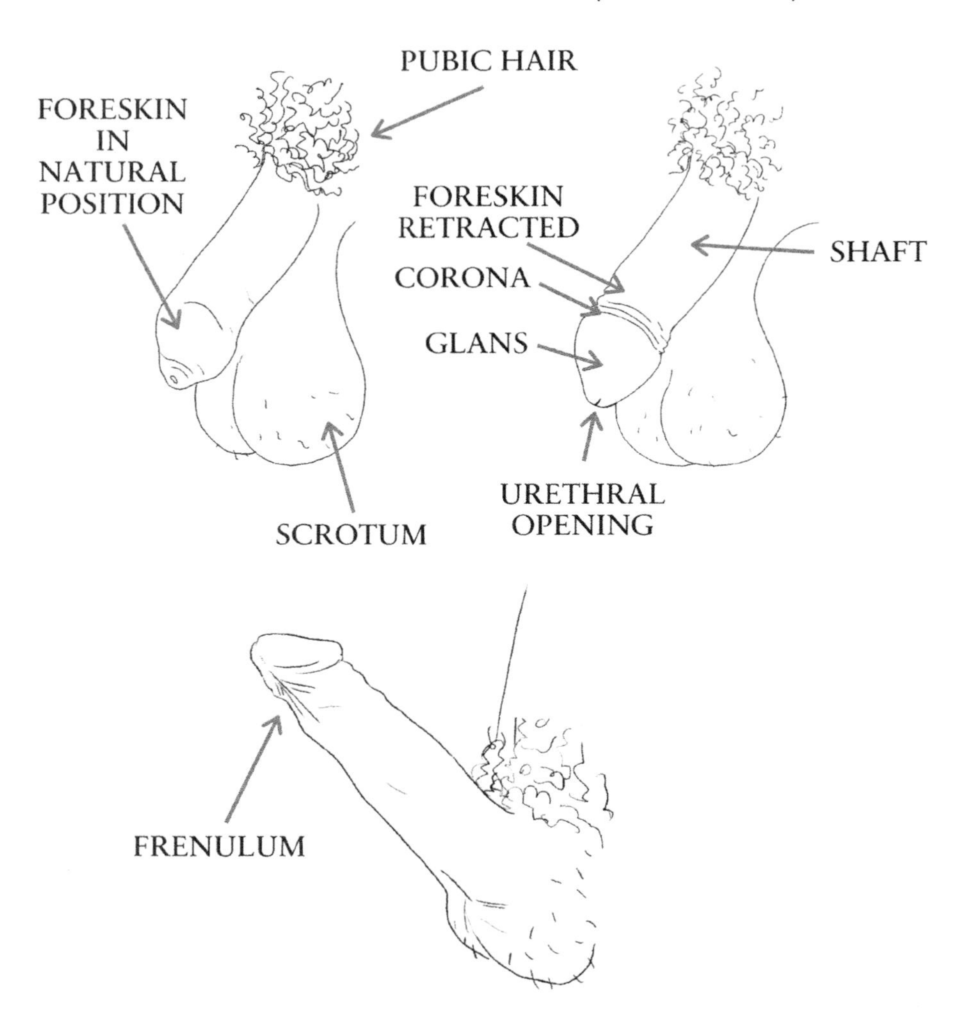

What do kids need to know?

Every child is different. Some kids will want to know every detail, whereas others will be happy with just the basics. The good thing is you won't be expected to remember all of this or have to talk about it all. That is where books become invaluable. Books will include all the technical details, which means you don't need to remember everything. A basic understanding will help with answering their questions.

So, what are the main messages we need to give to kids?

- Puberty means your body will change from being a kid to an adult.
- Changes are both physical and emotional.
- Puberty happens to all kids, and it is normal.
- Puberty means you can reproduce.
- Changes are very gradual.
- Puberty happens to all kids; to kids with a penis and to kids with a vagina.
- Puberty doesn't happen overnight; it takes two-to-five years from start to finish. This gives you time to get used to the new you.
- Some kids start puberty sooner, some start puberty later.
- Some kids change quickly, some kids change more slowly.
- Everyone is different.
- Your body is already programmed to create the body that you are meant to have. There is nothing you can do to change this

You can access my FREE sex education course for parents at https://sexedrescue.com/back-to-basics/

WHY DO I NEED TO TALK ABOUT PUBERTY?

Don't waste this opportunity to be your child's number-one source for information on love' sex and relationships.

Sometimes it can feel as if there are more reasons not to talk than there are to talk. Will you say too much and overwhelm them? Will you say too little and misinform them? Do females need to understand puberty differently than males? How do you approach the topic without embarrassing them or yourself? What if your child shows no interest or covers their ears while walking away?

You're not alone if you have already asked yourself some of these questions, as they are questions that parents commonly ask. If you have some lingering doubts about whether you're doing the right thing, you should know that most parents feel the same. Talking to your child about puberty is one of the greatest gifts you can give them, and yourself.

Here are some of the reasons why you should be talking to your child about puberty sooner rather than later:

Puberty will be much easier for them

Kids who know what to expect during puberty will usually have a much better experience than kids who are unprepared. Think back for a moment to your own memories of puberty. Did your parents talk to you about puberty and tell you what to expect? If they did, you are one of the lucky few! Most of us don't have very good memories of our own journey through puberty. We didn't have parents who spoke to us about puberty. Or if we did, it was usually the one big talk that we didn't really understand, which meant that we had to go through puberty unprepared for what was going to happen to us. So, we know that kids will cope much better with puberty when they know what to expect. They need to know about what changes are going to happen to them, why it is happening, and how to take care of their new body. You aren't alone if you want your child to have a much better experience of puberty than the one you had.

They'll hear about puberty anyway

Unless you live in the middle of nowhere with no contact with the outside world, your child will eventually hear about puberty. They will hear their friends talk about it at school as they whisper about growing hair down there or about their first trainer bra, or as they giggle and point out the pimples on their peer's faces. They will hear about it in class. Reproduction and the changes that happen to our bodies is in most school curriculums around the world. Don't be surprised if one day they bring a letter home from school advising you about these forthcoming lessons. They may learn about puberty from their favorite TV show, on the internet, or in a book.

Regardless of whether you have talked about puberty or not, your child is eventually going to hear about it. The problem is that what they hear will often be negative and inaccurate. This means that it is really important for you, the parent, to be the one who tells them about puberty. This is your opportunity to provide them with the right information in a way that prepares them instead of scaring them. More importantly, puberty is a great time to start talking to your child about what sexual behaviors and attitudes are okay, and not okay, in your family. Your child is now reaching the age where they will start forming their own attitudes and beliefs about sexuality. By sharing yours with them, you are providing them with a moral compass to guide them as they make sense of the mixed messages they receive from the media, their peers, and the world around them.

Kids want us to talk to them about growing up

Research tells us that 12-to-15-year-olds consistently say their parents are the most important influence when it comes to making decisions about sex, even more than their friends, the media, religious leaders, their siblings or sisters, or their teachers. Parental influence does decline as kids get older, though, which means that it is important to start talking sooner rather than later. [1]

Kids are now shaping their lifelong values

This is the time your child will be working out their own thoughts, beliefs and attitudes about the world around them. They will be making important decisions about what attitudes and behaviors are okay, and not okay, when it comes to love, sex and relationships. Which is why it is so important that you are there to guide them. You can't tell your child what their values and beliefs will be; you can only guide them. Do you have the exact same values as your parents? Probably not. You may share some of the same values as your parents, but you will also have some that are yours alone. And your siblings will have a completely different set of values, too, despite the fact that you were all influenced by your parents in the same way. The reason that you share some of the same values as your parents is because they influenced you. Some of their values must have made sense, and you took them on board as your own. And some you developed by yourself, influenced by what you saw on TV, heard in music, or learned by talking with your friends and by watching your peers.

Your child will be the same. They will make up her own set of values, but they will still listen to what you say. If you don't share your values with them, you can't expect to have any influence on what sexual attitudes and behaviors they develop. If you want to have any say in it, you will have to talk to them, and explain why you feel the way you do.

A stronger relationship

By having open and honest conversations about it, you can guide your child through puberty and strengthen your relationship. As much as you'd like to leave it up to someone such as the school or their friends to address the issue, you love your child and know they deserve to hear from you about the changes happening to them. This way, they'll be confident about what comes next, knowing that they can turn to you for support, guidance and information.

Research tells us that it is easier for teens to delay sexual activity and to avoid teen pregnancy when they are able to have open, honest conversations about these topics with their parents. Overall closeness between parent and child, shared activities, parental presence in the home, and parental caring and concern, were all associated with a reduced risk of early sex and teen pregnancy. Teens who are close to their parents and feel supported by them are more likely to delay sex, to have fewer sexual partners, and to use contraception. [2]

You already know a lot about puberty

You have firsthand experience of puberty. You have already been through it and know what it can be like. You know what it is like to find that first hair, the embarrassment of being teased for wearing a bra (or having an erection), or feeling embarrassed as someone you really like walks past and looks at you. Sharing stories from your own journey through puberty helps your child know that you have been there, and that you understand what they are going through.

A more confident child

Kids who know what to expect from puberty are going to be a lot more accepting of the changes they will soon be experiencing. They will feel a lot more positive about their bodies and feel good about their gender and biological sex. They will also be a lot more accepting of their own individual differences and be happy with who they are instead of unhappy about who they aren't! [3] It is helpful for kids to know that what is happening to them is normal, and that it is happening to their friends too.

Good practice for even trickier conversations

The more you talk about tough topics like puberty, the easier it gets. Eventually, you will be able to talk to your child without feeling as embarrassed, awkward or nervous. By the time you get to around to some of the other tough topics, such as dating and sex, you'll have had a bit of experience, and you will find it a lot easier than if you were starting afresh. There are plenty of good reasons why you should be talking to your child about puberty sooner rather than later.

You can access my FREE sex education course for parents at https://sexedrescue.com/back-to-basics/

References

1 The National Campaign to Prevent Teen and Unplanned Pregnancy. (2016). Survey Says: Parent Power Washington, DC: Author.

2 Albert, B. (2012). With One Voice 2012: America's Adults and Teens Sound Off About Teen Pregnancy. Washington, DC: The National Campaign to Prevent Teen and Unplanned Pregnancy.

3 Goldman, R & Goldman, J. (1988). Show me yours! Understanding children's sexuality. Ringwood. Penguin Books.

WHEN SHOULD I START TALKING ABOUT PUBERTY?

Puberty will start when your body is ready for it. You can't rush it' stop it' or make it slow down!

When is a good time to start talking?

There are a few signs that you can look out for that will let you know.

You should be ready to start talking to your child about puberty if:

1. You notice a change in moodiness (or their friends' parents start complaining of moodiness in their child).
2. They are starting to grow pubic and/or underarm hair.
3. They are starting to develop breasts.
4. They have pimples or a strong body odor.
5. They have had a sudden growth spurt and outgrow their shoes very quickly.
6. You notice that their friends are suddenly a lot taller, growing breasts, that they smell and/or have pimples.

7. They are aged eight and older (if they have a vagina)
8. They are aged nine and older (if they have a penis).
9. They start to ask you questions about puberty.

What age should I expect to see changes?

It depends on whether your child has a penis or a vagina.

If they have a penis, you'll start to see physical changes in your child anywhere between the ages of 10 and 14, but usually between 12 and 13.

If they have a vagina, you'll start to see physical changes in your child anywhere between the ages of eight and 14, but usually between 10 and 12.

Remember, every child is different. Some kids will be earlier or later than their friends. Some may have their changes in a slightly different order. Every child is different, and it is usually perfectly normal.

When is it too early to talk?

You can start talking to kids about puberty from a very young age. By talking when they are younger, you are gently introducing the concept to them that one day their body will start to change from being a child's body to an adult body. Kids as young as three or four will have no trouble grasping this concept. They won't really understand why, or even want to know, but they will accept it as just another thing that will one day happen to them. They will see puberty as being normal.

There are many possible opportunities for talking about puberty to young children. Your three-year-old might walk into the bathroom when you're changing your tampon or pad. They might ask why you're bleeding down there. Your five-year-old might be upset because their 13-year-old brother or sister won't have a bath with them anymore, and they want to know why. Your seven-year-old might have noticed that some of the older girls at school are growing breasts and wants to know if this will happen to them too. These are all situations where you can provide your child with basic information that will satisfy their curiosity. You don't need to worry about giving them too much information. Anything that they don't understand will be forgotten because it just won't make sense to them.

When is it too late to talk?

Sometimes you can wait too long to start talking about puberty, especially if your child has already started to menstruate or to have wet dreams. If this is your situation, it still isn't too late. It is better to be late than to never talk at all. You still have the opportunity to be able to prepare your child for what comes next and to let them know that they can turn to you for support, guidance and information.

Can men talk to females about puberty? Or women talk to males?

A lot of parents worry about whether it is okay to talk to a child of the opposite sex about puberty.

There is no reason why fathers or father figures can't talk to a female child about puberty. Some kids are comfortable talking about their changing body with their opposite-sex parent, and some kids aren't.

Let your child be the guide regarding what they are comfortable with. If you get the sense that they aren't comfortable, try to involve an adult of the same sex that they trust, such as an aunt or uncle, an older cousin, or a family friend.

You can access my FREE sex education course for parents at https://sexedrescue.com/back-to-basics/

WHAT CHANGES WILL HAPPEN DURING PUBERTY?

We all go through the same changes. For some they happen in a different order sooner or later faster or slower. But at the end of the day they'll all have a grown-up body.

Puberty is that time when your child will change into an adult. Luckily these changes happen slowly, over a two-to-10-year period, which means they have plenty of time to get used to their new body. The first changes that happen with puberty are hidden, as they happen on the inside.

There are many visible and invisible changes that will happen during this time. Some of the changes that happen to your child's body will be easy to spot, but others won't be, as they are hidden inside their body. Although the timing of puberty can be different, the sequence of changes that will happen to your child is more predictable. It is important to remember, though, that for some kids, it may be different. For example, some kids will grow armpit hair first, whereas for others it may be pubic hair. Whichever order it happens in, both are completely normal.

Below you will find a rough guide to the changes you can expect and when. Not every child will follow this pattern, but it will give you an idea of what to expect. Many of the changes during puberty will also overlap each other and may happen over several years. Remember, every child is different and almost anything can be normal. If concerned, talk to your family doctor.

Changes to bodies with a penis

Nine to 12 years

Hidden changes

The first changes that will happen to your child are hidden, as they are happening deep inside their body. The body will start to release hormones that will trigger changes to start happening. The main hormone for males is testosterone. It will begin to surge in your child's body, causing their testicles to grow and make sperm. No changes can yet be seen outside their body, other than some growth of the scrotum and testicles. Some kids may have a growth spurt, and some may start to grow very fine hairs in the pubic area.

Nine to 15 years

(Average 11 to 13 years)

Testicles

Your child's testicles will continue to slowly grow, with one testicle now beginning to hang lower than the other. This prevents the testicles from knocking against each other. Their scrotum will also hang lower, becoming darker in color, thinner and less smooth. If your child has pale skin, their scrotum will become more reddish in color, while with dark skin, it will deepen in color.

Penis

Your child's penis will remain unchanged. It may grow slightly larger, but usually there is little or no change at all. They may start to have erections more frequently, but they won't be making sperm.

Hair growth

Fine hair may begin to grow at the base of the penis and scrotum. These first hairs are usually long, slightly pigmented (colored) and straight or slightly curly. It is normal for some kids not to grow hair just yet.

Growth spurt

Your child will start to grow taller and the shape of their body will begin to change. Before they grow taller, their feet and hands will usually have a growth spurt of their own. Your child will also gain weight as they start to develop muscle, and as their bones grow bigger.

Some kids worry about the body fat that they gain during puberty, thinking that they need to go on a diet. It is important to remember that your child is supposed to gain weight during puberty. The weight and height growth spurts don't always happen at the same time or at the same pace. Sometimes they may feel as if they are getting fat, but then they'll have a growth spurt so the body fat will spread out to fit their new height. If weight gain is rapid, some kids will develop stretch marks. This can be seen as purplish or white lines on the skin. It isn't common but it can happen.

If you find yourself joking about them going up a shoe size overnight, then you can be certain that puberty is on its way!

Body odor

It is during puberty that your child will start to sweat. This means that their body odor will change, especially when it comes from their armpits.

Chest

The skin around the nipples, known as the areola, will darken and start to increase in size.

11 to 16 years

(Average 13 ½ to 15 ½ years)

Testicles

Your child's testicles and scrotum will continue to grow. Sperm production may begin for some, but not all, which means they will be able to ejaculate. Most kids usually discover this during masturbation, or they might wake up in the morning with wet pants after a wet dream (nocturnal emission).

Penis

Your child's penis will start to grow. It will grow longer, rather than wider. Erections will be a lot more common than before, often at the wrong time, or in the wrong place.

Hair growth

Some kids may only now be starting to develop pubic hair. It will become darker, thicker and curlier, and start to cover a much wider area. Hair will continue to grow on their legs and underarms.

Growth spurt

Your child's body will still be growing and gaining weight and height. Muscles become larger and shoulders broader. They will grow taller and you'll notice that they are a lot hungrier and eating more food as their body tries to keep up with the energy it needs to grow. Their face will also begin to change, making them look more mature.

Body odor and skin

Sweat and oil glands will become more active, which can result in acne. Body odor is here to stay.

Voice

Their voice will begin to crack as the voice box gets larger.

Chest

It can be common for some kids to experience short-term swelling and tenderness around the nipples. As their shoulders grow wider, this breast tissue will flatten, usually disappearing within one or two years.

11 to 17 years

(Average 15 to 17 years)

Testicles

Your child's testicles and scrotum will continue to grow. The scrotum skin will continue to darken. They will now begin to produce sperm, which means that wet dreams (nocturnal emissions) may start to happen, and they will ejaculate with masturbation and sexual arousal. Not all kids will have wet dreams (either is normal).

Penis

Their penis will become thicker and longer. The glans, at the end of the penis, will grow wider and develop a distinct edge or corona.

Hair growth

Pubic hair continues to grow, with hair now starting to grow around the anus, and possibly even in a line from the groin up to the navel. Hair will continue to grow on their legs and underarms. Facial hair will start to grow, usually on the upper lip, chin and near the ears.

Growth spurt

Your child will keep on gaining weight and growing taller.

Body odor and skin

We have oil glands all over our bodies, but during puberty, they become a lot more active. Your child's skin may become oily, especially around the chin, nose, forehead, chest and/or back. Some kids may develop acne or pimples. Their hair is also more likely to become oily, meaning they will now need to wash it more frequently.

Voice

Their voice will continue to crack at times and deepen.

14 to 18 years

(Average age 17 years)

This is the last stage of changes. Your child will now reach their full height and will look like a young adult. Their pubic hair will now cover their groin, and possibly even their inner thighs. Their genitals will now be fully grown and will look the same as adults with a penis. Your child may now need to shave (if they choose to), as their facial hair continues to grow. Some kids will begin to grow chest hair.

Changes to bodies with a vagina

Eight to 11 years

Hidden changes

The first changes that will happen to your child are hidden as they are happening deep inside their body. The body will start to release hormones that will trigger the changes to start happening. The main hormone for females is estrogen. It will begin to surge in your child's body, making their ovaries grow much larger, but no changes can yet be seen outside their body.

Eight to 14 years

(Average 11 to 12 years)

Breasts

Everyone is different, but the first visible sign of puberty that you will most likely see in your child is the development of breasts. A small number of kids can be different and will develop pubic hair before breasts. This is completely normal and nothing to worry about.

Breast development happens slowly, over three-to-five years. Breast buds will develop, and your child may feel a small lump behind their nipple. The nipples will be tender and elevated, and the area around the nipple, the areola, will increase in size. Breast buds are made up of breast tissue, which, over time, will begin to grow bigger and bigger, developing into a round and full breast.

Pubic hair

Your child will start to grow a small amount of fine, soft hair on the skin around the external genitals, on the mons pubis and the labia majora. Over the next couple of years, their pubic hair will grow thicker and darker. It may be coarse or fine, straight or curly. Everyone is different.

Growth spurt

The next thing to happen is usually a growth spurt. Some kids are different and may have a growth spurt at either the same time as, or just before, breasts. Regardless of what comes first, your child will grow a lot taller over the next two-to-three years, as well as gain weight. Before they grow taller, their feet and hands will usually have a growth spurt of their own.

If you find yourself joking about them going up a shoe size overnight, then you can be certain that puberty is on its way!

Your child's body shape will also begin to change, and they will become rounder and curvier. Their hips will grow wider, and they will now begin to show the beginning of a waistline. As their body begins to store fat, they will start to gain weight. Sometimes this weight gain happens quickly, over one-to-two years, or it may happen more slowly over three-to-four years. Some kids worry about the body fat that they gain during puberty, thinking that they need to go on a diet. It is important to remember that your child is supposed to gain weight during puberty. The weight and height growth spurts don't always happen at the same time or at the same pace. Sometimes they may feel as if they are getting fat, but then they'll have a growth spurt so the body fat will spread out to fit their new height. If weight gain is rapid, some kids will develop stretch marks. This can be seen as purplish or white lines on the skin. It isn't common but it can happen.

Body odor

It is during puberty that your child will now start to sweat. This means that their body odor will change, especially when it comes from their armpits.

Nine to 15 years

(Average 12 to 13 years)

Breasts

Your child's breasts will continue to grow, increasing in size and being more cone-shaped and pointy. Their nipple and areola will now be more obvious, becoming larger and darker.

Pubic hair

Their pubic hair will begin to grow coarser and darker, but there still isn't a lot of it. They may also start to grow more hair on their lower legs.

Growth spurt

Their body will still be growing and gaining weight and height.

Reproductive organs

Inside your child's body, their reproductive organs will grow larger. Their vagina, ovaries, fallopian tubes, and uterus will all grow.

Genitals

Outside their body, their genitals will also begin to change. Their vulva will swell as the different parts begin to grow. Their mons pubis will begin to show a bulge, with the fat pad getting thicker and softer. The labia majora, the outer lips, will become fleshier and wrinkly, with their edges beginning to touch or meet up. As the oil glands begin to work, your child may notice small, light-colored, slightly raised bumps on the underside of the skin. The labia minora, the inner lips, will become fleshier, wrinkly and more noticeable. Their oil glands will start working, making these tissues moister. They will also darken in color. The clitoris will be larger and more sensitive.

Vaginal discharge

As the vagina grows, your child may notice vaginal discharge for the first time. They may notice a white or yellow stain on their underwear, or comment about feeling wet around the vulval area. This is all completely normal and is just the body's way of looking after itself. Some kids worry when this first happens. They think that they may have wet themselves, or that there is something wrong with them. It is important for your child to know that they are normal and that their vaginal discharge will change during their menstrual cycle. Sometimes it will be lighter or heavier.

Vaginal discharge is usually the last change that happens before the first period, so your child can expect their first period in about six-to-12 months' time. Some kids will start to have vaginal discharge for as long as two-to-three years before their first period. In this case, the discharge will usually become more frequent and in heavier amounts in the last few months leading up to their period.

Menstruation or periods

Some kids may have their first menstrual period.

> If your daughter has breasts, some pubic hair and vaginal discharge, you need to prepare her for her period.

10 to 16 years

(Average 13 to 14 years)

Breasts

Their nipple and areola will become more obvious, becoming larger, darker and pointier. Eventually, their breasts will have a fuller, more rounded adult shape. Sometimes breasts grow at different rates, one then the other. They will usually end up a similar size.

Pubic and underarm hair

Their pubic hair will grow thick, curly and become coarser, taking on a more adult triangular pattern of growth. Underarm hair may now start to appear. Some kids may already have underarm hair, but usually, they start to grow underarm hair one-to-two years after pubic hair.

Growth spurt

Your child will continue to grow and their hips will become rounder, but not at the same rate as before.

Menstruation or periods

If they haven't already started, then the first menstrual period should now start. Most kids start getting their periods about two-to-two-and-a-half years after the start of breasts. Some kids may start just one year later, while others start three-to-four years later. Most kids have their first period between the ages of 12 and 13, but some will start as early as age nine, and others as late as 15.

When your child's period finally does arrive, it is likely to be irregular at first. The timing of their period and the amount of blood loss will vary. For the first few months, or even up to a year, they probably won't ovulate. Once they do start to ovulate, they will then be fertile and capable of becoming pregnant. Some kids ovulate with their first period. If their periods are regular, then there is a good chance that they are ovulating.

Oily skin and hair

We have oil glands all over our bodies, but during puberty, they become a lot more active. Your child's skin may become oily, especially around the chin, nose, forehead, chest and/or back. Some kids may develop acne or pimples. Their hair is also more likely to become oily, meaning that they will now need to wash it more frequently.

12 to 19 years

(Average age 15 years)

This is the last stage of changes. Your child will now reach their full height and will look like a young adult. They will now be ovulating, which means that their menstrual period will be regular. Their breasts will be fully grown, and pubic hair will have an adult triangular pattern of growth. Their skin will be less oily, which usually means less pimples, except for the occasional one.

Changes to their feelings and relationships

Puberty is not just about getting your child's body ready to make babies. It is also about making sure that they are ready to face all the responsibilities that come with being an adult.

While your child's body is changing, their brain will be changing too. They will experience changes in:

- The way they feel about themself.
- Their relationship with their parents.
- Their friendships and feelings of love.
- What others expect of them.

This is also the time that they will be working out their own thoughts, beliefs and attitudes about the world around them. They will be making important decisions about what attitudes and behaviors are okay, and not okay, when it comes to love, sex and relationships. It is important that you are there to provide your child with the support, guidance and information they need.

Kids who are prepared for puberty are more likely to find it a breeze instead of a hurricane!

Common feelings

Puberty is not necessarily the nightmare that we are all led to believe it is. Everyone is different regarding how they respond to this time in their life. The one thing we do know is that kids who know what to expect from puberty have a much easier time as they go through it. If your child has a much easier time, it means that you will too!

Common feelings that your child may experience during puberty include:

- Struggling with a sense of identity and questions about themself.
- Moodiness, anger and depression.
- Sleeping a bit more than usual.
- Wishing they were older and being in a hurry to grow up.
- A need for more independence and privacy.
- Relationships with their friends and the opinions of others becoming more important than family.

- Being more concerned or worried about how they look, with a focus on clothes and their body.
- Worrying about what the future holds (school, family, job, etc.).
- Having crushes on actors, singers, teachers, peers, other kids.
- Being curious about changes that are happening to their body, especially their genitals.
- Feeling sexually attracted to people.
- Being more interested in sex than ever before and perhaps fantasizing and masturbating.
- Masturbation taking on a new meaning due to orgasm and sexual feelings.

As you can see, there is a lot happening. What's important is that your child understands this is all normal and it happens to everyone. Their friends will be going through the same things too. It is normal for kids to feel anxious about growing up, and to sometimes wonder if they are going crazy. Think back to your own memories of puberty, and you will know what I mean. Puberty is a time of great change and the more support your child has, the easier a time it will be for them and ultimately for you too.

You can access my FREE sex education course for parents at https://sexedrescue.com/back-to-basics/

References

A Blessing Not a Curse: A Mother-Daughter Guide to the Transition from Child to Woman by Jane Bennett. 2002. Sally Milner Publishing Pty Ltd. Bowral.

Adolescence and Puberty. Edited by John Bancroft and June Machover Reinisch. 1990. Oxford University Press. New York.

Gender Differences at Puberty. Edited by Chris Haywood. 2003. Cambridge University Press. Cambridge.

Handbook of Child and Adolescent Sexuality: Developmental and Forensic Psychology. Edited by Daniel S. Bromberg and William T. O'Donohue. 2013. Elsevier. Academic Press. Oxford.

Puberty: Physiology and Abnormalities by Philip Kumanov and Ashok Agarwal. 2016. Springer International Publishing. Switzerland.

WHAT SHOULD I BE TALKING ABOUT?

This is all normal and their friends are going through it too. Soon they will be used to their new body and know how to care for it.

A new self-care regimen

Puberty is all about change, and your child will soon have a new body to care for. They will need a little bit of advice on how to care for it. Remember, all of this is new to them. What you and I think of as common sense, such as washing hair more regularly so it doesn't smell and get oily, isn't as obvious to your child. They need you to slowly start teaching them a whole new regimen of self-care, and they will need a fair bit of reminding before they automatically start to include these new habits into their everyday life.

What to talk about

Relax: you don't need to talk to your child about every single thing that is listed below. Let them guide you regarding what is relevant to them. If they are asking about a bra, talk to them about what will happen as their breasts start to grow. If they are asking about deodorant, talk to them about how they will soon start to smell under the arms like an adult.

Go back to the previous chapter and try to work out which stage of development your child is at. Talk about the changes that are now happening as well as the ones to come.

Just remember, you don't need to talk to them about everything. The fact that you are talking to them is much more important than what you say. By talking about puberty, you're actually letting them know that they can turn to you for support, guidance and information.

Feelings

Your child needs to know from the very start that puberty will change their body, but it will also change their feelings as well.

It may help your child to know:

- All these new emotions are normal.
- Feeling anxious about growing up is normal. It is normal to not want to grow up or to even be excited or in a hurry to grow up. It can even be normal to feel as if they are going crazy at times.
- Everyone goes through puberty. Some of their friends will be feeling the same things as them. Or different things.
- Going through puberty can be hard.
- There are ways to express intense feelings. They may need some guidance as to what will work for them, such as going for a run or a swim, writing in a journal, or talking to someone.

- Mood swings may happen, where they might feel sad one moment and happy the next. Life for a few years can sometimes be a rollercoaster of changing emotions.
- They may want to spend more time on their own and alone. They need to know that is okay and that their parents still love them and are still there for them.
- Privacy will become a lot more important and they need to know their parents will respect their need for more personal space.
- Their brain will be changing and getting ready for them to be an adult. This means that they will want to start making their own decisions about things and to try new things.
- Having sexual feelings is normal and is nothing to feel guilty about. Acting on such feelings, however, is a big responsibility.

For advice on understanding puberty for your child (both males and females), the book Untangled by Lisa Damour is excellent. It will give you insight into what is happening to your child psychologically and how to cope as a parent.

Skin care

Your child's skin will now become oily as their oil glands become more active. The oil glands below the surface of the skin will enlarge and start to make sebum, a white oily substance that keeps the skin moist. Sometimes the sebum gets blocked in the oil glands, which means whiteheads or blackheads appear, and if there is infection, then pimples will appear. This means that they'll have oilier skin, sometimes with acne.

As you start to notice their skin becoming oily, it may help your child to know:

- They need to wash their face each day.
- They shouldn't pick at or squeeze pimples (risk of infection and scarring).
- If they are going to wear make-up, it needs to be as natural as possible (oil-based makeup will clog their pores).

Sometimes acne can become severe, and if that happens, you can visit your family doctor for treatment.

How much acne will your child have? Chances are that they will have the same amount that either of their parents had. So, if you didn't have much acne, chances are that your child won't either.

Body odor

Your child will now start to sweat more and develop body odor for the first time. Sweat glands can be found under their arms, on the palms of their hands, at the bottom of their feet and between their legs. During puberty, these sweat glands become more active, and due to the bacteria on the skin, they will start to develop body odor or BO. This means that at times, they'll stink!

As you start to notice their body smelling, it may help your child to know:

- They need to shower each day.

- They need to use deodorant or antiperspirant on clean armpits (it doesn't work as well on smelly armpits).
- They may need to look for aluminum-free deodorant (aluminum is linked with breast cancer and Alzheimer's disease).
- They will need to wear clean underwear each day.
- They may need to wash their sports shoes or wear cotton/wool/dry-wicking socks if their feet start to smell.
- They shouldn't use vaginal deodorant sprays as they can irritate their vulva.
- Everyone sweats, so they aren't alone.

Sometimes kids struggle with adapting to the changes that puberty brings. Remind your child that it can take time to get used to their new body.

Oily Hair

The oil glands that make your child's skin oilier are the same ones that may now make their hair oilier. Each strand of hair has its own oil gland, which keeps the hair shiny and waterproof. During puberty, extra oil is produced, which then makes the hair on their head oily. This means that they'll have hair that may look too shiny, oily and greasy.

As you start to notice their hair smelling or looking oily, it may help your child to know:

- They need to wash their hair more often, possibly daily or every second to third day.

- They may need to use a special shampoo for oily hair.
- They may need to look for hair styling products that are oil-free or greaseless.

Body hair

As your child goes through puberty, they will start to grow hair in some new places.

People with a penis

As your child with a penis goes through puberty, they will start to grow hair in some new places. Pubic hair, meaning hair around the penis and scrotum, usually happens first, with face and chest hair happening much later in puberty. The hair on their arms and legs may also increase and/or change. The amount of hair that your child grows depends on their cultural background and genetics. Some cultures have more hair than others. Have a look at the adults with a penis on both sides of your child's family. If they have a lot of body hair, there is a good chance that your child will have a similar amount. Some adults with a penis have a lot of hair and some don't. Everything is pretty much normal!

Your child will start to grow facial hair between the ages of 14 and 16. Every child is different, with some kids starting earlier and some later.

As you start to notice new body hair, it may help your child to know:

- They will grow hair at the base of their penis and scrotum. It will start off fine and soft, and over the next couple of years, their pubic hair will grow thicker and darker. It may be coarse or fine, straight or curly. Every kid is different.

- They will start to grow hair under their arms.
- They will grow more hair on their arms and legs, and it may be darker in color.
- They will grow hair on their face, i.e., a beard and a moustache. They may want to remove this by shaving, but you'll talk about it when this hair starts growing.
- The amount of hair that grows is different for everyone.
- Every person is different. Some kids will have more body hair than others.

People with a vagina

For children with a vagina, pubic hair (hair around the outside of their vulva) usually happens first, but for some kids, underarm hair grows first. Every child is different, and both are normal. Depending on your cultural background, your child may grow hair in some other places too. Some kids will grow hair on their upper lip, their chin or on the side of their face. Or they may grow hair around their nipple and on or between their breasts. If the adults with a vagina on either side of your child's family have hair in these places, then there is a good chance that your child will too. If your child grows hair in these other places, and there is no family history for this, you should probably see your family doctor, as it needs to be investigated.

The arrival of body hair means you'll need to make a decision about what your family rules are about body hair.

- How do you feel about your child removing their body hair?

- If yes, from what age?
- Which body hair can they remove?
- How can they remove their body hair? Shaving, waxing, or any of the other methods?

As you start to notice new body hair, it may help your child to know:

- They will grow hair around their vulva and underarms. It will start off fine and soft, and over the next couple of years, their pubic hair will grow thicker and darker. It may be coarse or fine, straight or curly. Every kid is different.
- They will grow more hair on her arms and legs, and it may be darker in color. This hair may lighten as they become an adult, but it may not.
- The amount of hair that grows is different for everyone.
- What your family rules are for the removal of body hair. Be prepared for the fact that they may have their own ideas about this.
- Some kids like to remove their body hair. They may experience peer group pressure to shave their legs or armpits. They may want to remove their body hair because they think it will make them look and feel more grown up. Talk about the attitudes of your community or culture regarding body hair (most societies feel that women shouldn't have body hair).
- They need to know about the consequences of hair removal. Once removed, hair will grow back darker.
- Every person is different. Some people will have more body hair than others.

Breasts

People with a vagina

For most kids with a vagina, breasts will be the first change they notice. For some kids, their first change will be pubic hair, or even underarm hair. Whichever is first, breasts or hair, both are normal. Breasts grow slowly over a few years before they are fully grown. Most kids will start growing breasts when they are between 10 and 11, but some can start when they are as young as eight or as old as 13.

If you were a late bloomer, chances are your child will be too!

It is the hormone estrogen that tells your body to grow breasts. Breasts will start off as breast buds, where a small lump will begin to grow behind the nipple. These buds are made of breast tissue which, over time, begin to grow bigger and bigger, developing into a round and full breast.

Luckily, breasts grow slowly over three-to-five years, which means your child has plenty of time to get used to them.

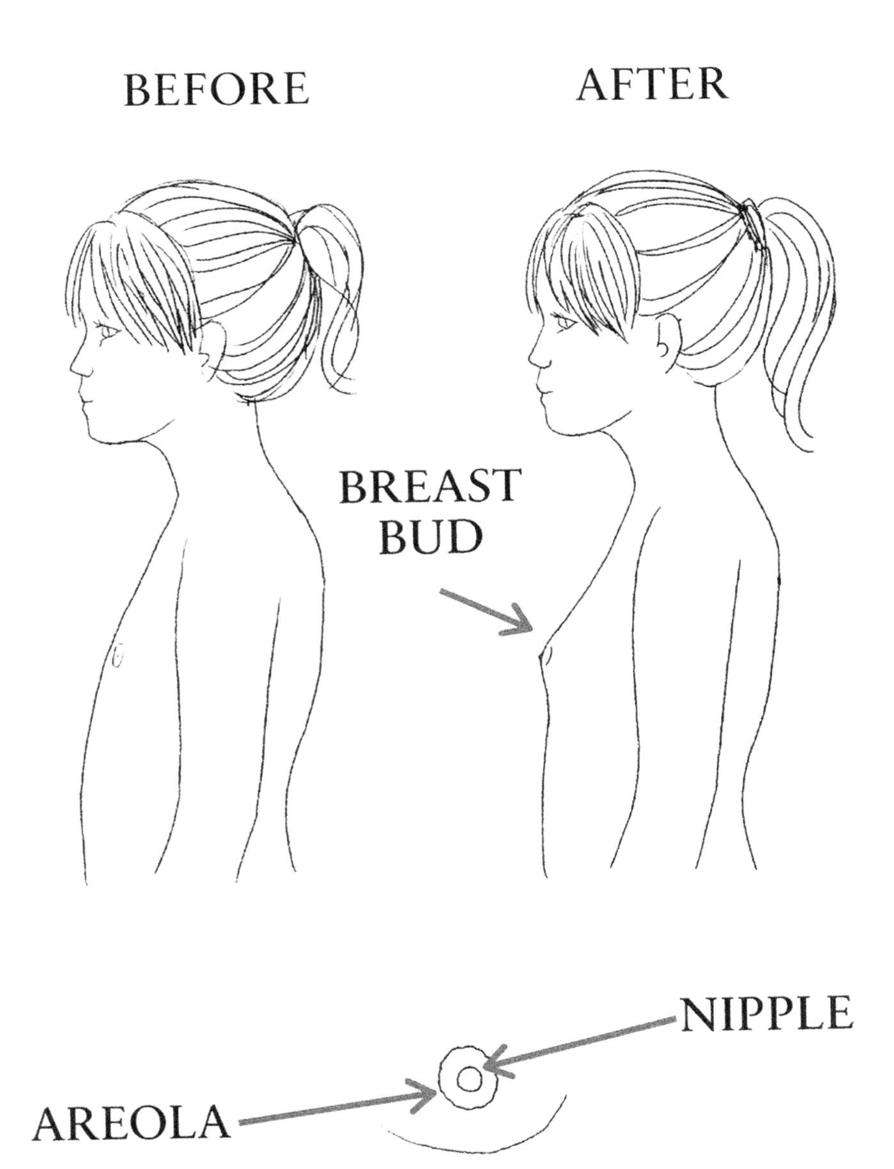
BEFORE
AFTER
BREAST
BUD
NIPPLE
AREOLA

As you start to notice breast buds, it may help your child to know:

- Breast buds will develop, and they may feel a small lump behind their nipple. The nipples will be tender and elevated, and the area around the nipple, the areola, will increase a little in size.
- Their breasts will grow, swell and hurt just a bit. They may feel itchy as the skin stretches with the new growth.
- They may look pointy or lumpy while they are growing. They will become rounder and fuller once they are fully grown. Breasts come in different shapes and sizes. Theirs may look completely different from what they expect.
- The color of their areola will change from purplish to grey to light pink to dark brown depending on their skin color. The areola will get bigger and darker as their breast grows. Their nipples will also start to poke out more and be much more noticeable over time.
- Some kids may have discharge from their nipples, if the nipple is squeezed. This is usually normal, and the fluid is made by the body to keep the breast ducts clear. If they keep on squeezing their breasts, they might make their breasts start producing more, so they shouldn't keep doing it.
- Breasts can feel tender and sore, especially when their body is getting ready for a period.
- Breasts may not grow evenly or at the same rate or to the same size. Sometimes one breast may grow more quickly than the other, which means they might look a little lopsided. But they are usually the same size by the time they finish growing.

- By the time their breasts stop growing, one breast is usually slightly smaller than the other. This is normal.
- They may feel self-conscious when their breasts first begin to grow. Sometimes wearing a tank top or trainer bra or a loose shirt can make them feel less shy or embarrassed.
- They will eventually need to wear a bra for breast support.
- Every person is different. Some people will start to grow breasts sooner or later than their friends, some kids will grow their breasts faster or slower than their friends, and some will grow larger or smaller breasts than their friends. Every kid is different!
- Their body will start to grow breasts when it is ready. You can't rush breasts! They will grow at the right time.
- Some kids will feel excited or embarrassed about growing breasts. How does your child feel?
- Some people will make comments about their changing body. Sometimes these comments are nice, or they can be teasing or even mean. How do you think they'll manage this? What can they do if this happens to them? Who can they talk to?
- Some kids are unhappy with their breast size. They shouldn't let their breast size affect how they feel about themself.
- Their friends are going through the same thing!

People with a penis

It is common for kids with a penis to have slight chest swelling at the start of puberty due to hormones. It doesn't mean that your child is growing breasts. It is just extra fat tissue that will flatten out in 12-to-18 months' time, when their shoulders grow wider. Kids usually find this quite alarming, as they think that they are growing breasts and that they are there to stay.

If you start to notice breasts, it may help your child to know:

- One in two people with a penis will start to grow breasts.
- This is completely normal and will go away in 12-to-18 months. They won't have breasts forever and they won't need to wear a bra.
- Most kids find this embarrassing.
- If they feel self-conscious, they can try wearing loose fitting shirts, so that it is isn't as noticeable.
- Some kids also get tenderness behind the nipple area. This is normal too.
- The skin behind their nipple, the areola, will grow darker and wider.
- Some people will make comments about their changing body. Sometimes these comments are nice, or they can be teasing or even mean. Talk to your child about how to manage this. What can they do if this happens to him? Who can they talk to?
- Every person is different. This will happen to some kids but not all. There is nothing they can do, other than wait for their shoulders to grow wider, which is when this breast tissue will flatten out.
- Some of their friends are going through the same thing.

Body size and shape

Your child needs to know that they will be having two types of growth spurts. They will grow taller and they will also start to get heavier as their body builds muscle and stores fat.

As you start to notice their body shape and size changing, it may help your child to know:

- The bodies of kids with a penis will gain weight and grow taller and stronger.
- The bodies of kids with a vagina will gain weight and grow taller, hips will broaden, and breasts will get bigger.
- They may feel self-conscious about their new shape, size and fat.
- They may have some growing pains while this happens. The cause is unknown, but they may feel it in the legs (calf, front of thigh or behind knees). It may be worse in the afternoon or evening and may wake them during the night. Massage, heat packs and mild analgesia can help.
- They will gain weight, and this is what their body is supposed to do. Their body is going to start building muscle and storing fat. Bones will also grow longer and thicker.
- They may develop stretch marks as their body grows quickly. These will eventually fade over time.
- At times, they may feel fat. This is normal and when their body has its next growth spurt for height, any extra fat will usually spread out. We all have different body shapes, and you can't change the body shape that you are meant to have.

- They don't need to worry about dieting. As long as they have a healthy, well-balanced diet and enough exercise, their body will do what it is meant to do.
- There is a wide range of body shapes and sizes.
- Their face will change, becoming longer and narrower than it was before.

Voice changes

People with a penis

Your child's voice will change during puberty as their larynx (Adam's apple) increases in size. Their vocal cords will become longer and thicker, and the tone of their voice will begin to change. Their voice will begin to break or crack, then become low. This usually happens around 14 or 15 but can happen earlier or later. It may happen suddenly, or they may not even notice it.

It may help your child to know that:

- Their voice might crack when they speak. This is when their voice will suddenly shift to a higher pitch, and temporarily sound high and squeaky.
- Some kids find this really embarrassing, while others aren't all that bothered.
- Try not to make this a big deal when it happens. The more they worry, the more it will crack.
- It is a sign that they are growing up.
- It is happening to other kids too.

- Voices also change for people with a vagina, but not as much as for people with a penis.

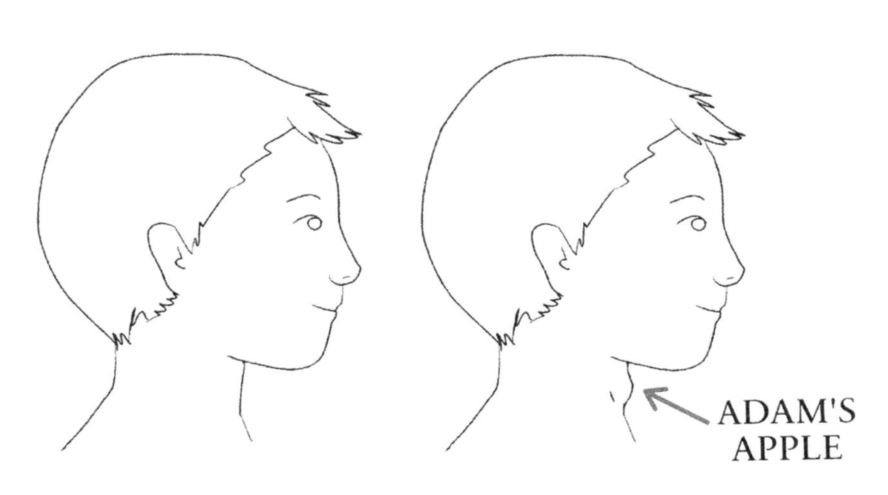

People with a vagina

Your child's voice will deepen slightly during puberty. The chances are that neither of you will even notice it changing, as it will happen slowly over a number of years.

Vulva and vagina

Your child needs to know that their vulva and vagina will be changing too. As well as growing bigger, parts will change color and it will look, feel and smell differently.

Teach your child to clean their vulva in the following way:

1. When showering or bathing, wash your vulva with warm water and mild or unscented soap. (Some people choose to not use soap, so it's up to you as to whether you do or don't.)
2. Separate your labia and gently cleanse around the folds, using a clean washcloth or your hands. Avoid getting water or soap inside your vagina. Then wash the anus and area between the anus and vulva.
3. Rinse completely, making sure no soap is left behind on the skin.

It may help your child to know:

- Vulvas come in all shapes, sizes and colors. It is unique, just like your face is unique to you.
- Vaginal discharge is healthy. All people with a vagina have it.
- The vagina is self-cleaning and doesn't need to be washed inside.
- They don't need to douche (flush water into the vagina) or use scented wipes and vaginal deodorants or sprays.
- Smegma (the white discharge found between the folds of the labia) is normal but should be washed away when washing.
- Everyone sweats in the vulva area, especially when exercising or if the weather is hot.

Vaginal discharge

Kids with a vagina can find it quite alarming when they first notice vaginal discharge. Your child may think they are wetting themself, as they become aware of the sensation of fluid coming out of their vagina. Or they may wonder what these white/yellow patches are that they find on the inside of their underwear. Vaginal discharge is a normal part of puberty. Basically, it is secretions from the lining of the vagina and cervix that will come out through the vagina. Often, kids are not even aware that it is coming out, but other times they may feel it as it comes out. Most people usually find it on their underwear. The amount of discharge, the color, and the texture of it changes during the menstrual cycle. It can range from being clear and slippery like egg white to being white, and either creamy or thick and pasty. When it dries, it will look white or yellow. All of this is completely normal and is different for everyone.

Vaginal discharge is usually the last change that happens before the first period, so your child can expect their first period in about six-to-12 months' time. Some kids will start to have vaginal discharge for as long as two-to-three years before their first period. In this case, the discharge will usually become more frequent and in heavier amounts in the last few months leading up to their period.

When is a good time to start talking about this with your child?

Well, if you have already noticed white/yellow stains on their underwear, or you hear the odd comment from them about feeling wet down below, or if they have started to grow breasts and pubic or underarm hair, then now is a good time to start talking.

It may help your child to know:

- They might see and feel a clear or white liquid from their vagina or white/yellowish staining on underwear. This is normal and means that their vagina and cervix are working properly.
- Their vaginal discharge will always change. Some days they will notice it and other days they won't. Some days it will be heavier and some days it will be lighter. Sometimes it will feel like egg white and other days it will be thick and pasty.
- Discharge doesn't happen every day, just some days of the menstrual cycle.
- Their vaginal discharge will change when they ovulate, signaling that they are now fertile (it changes to help the sperm to reach the egg).
- Paying attention to their vaginal discharge can help them to better understand their body.
- If it changes color or smells, or they become itchy or their skin becomes irritated, it might mean that they have an infection. They should seek medical attention, just in case it is an infection.
- They need to wash their vulva daily, making sure they wash around the folds of the labia. They can use a low ph soap and water for this. There is no need for powders or deodorants.
- If the discharge is heavy, and making their pants feel wet, they can wear a panty liner or even period pants (underwear with an inbuilt absorbent lining that won't leak).
- Increased vaginal discharge usually means their period will start sometime in the next six-to-12 months.

- When toileting, wipe from front to back.
- All people with a vagina have vaginal discharge. It is normal.

Periods

All kids with a vagina want to know when they will get their period. It is a much-anticipated event and seen by many as the sign that they have finally become an adult. They will usually have a lot of questions about periods, but their main concern will be about when they will start. They will have a lot of unanswered questions and fears about what periods will mean. And they will hear stories from their peers about the horrible things that can happen when you have your period. The more information your child has about periods, the more prepared they will be when their time comes. Below you will find information that will address most of the most common concerns that kids usually have about their periods.

What is menstruation?

It may help your child to know:

- Menstruation is when the uterus sheds its lining each month and it comes out of the vagina as blood and endometrial tissue.
- Their period can last between three and seven days.
- It usually happens about once a month.
- It means that they can become pregnant if they have sexual intercourse.
- Periods stop during pregnancy and return once you've had the baby.

When will they get their period?

It may help your child to know:

- Every person is different – some start earlier, and some start later.
- For some people, they may be as young as nine or 10.
- Other people may be 14 or 15.
- Most kids get their period when they are 12 or 13.
- Some signs that will give them a clue about when their period is on its way:
  - Their breasts have already been growing for about two years.
  - They've had some pubic and underarm hair for the last four-to-six months.
  - They've been having some vaginal discharge for the last three months. Some can have this up to two-to-three years before their first period. In this case, if it starts to get heavier and more frequent, then that is a sign that their period is on its way.
  - They may get premenstrual symptoms beforehand, like tummy cramps, back ache, headaches, feeling bloated, slight nausea, tiredness and possibly feel irritable, sad, and/or tense.
  - Find out when their birth mother started their period – there is a good chance that they'll start theirs at around the same age. This isn't always accurate, but it is a helpful guide.
- Every person is different, and their period will start when their body is ready for it.

How will they know when their period has started?

The answer to this question may seem pretty obvious, but it isn't to your inexperienced child. Think about it for a moment...their current experiences of blood are when they hurt themself. So, they probably have quite a few fears about what it means to have blood come out of their vagina each month. Plus, they will have heard a lot of scary stories about what it is like. It is a good idea to provide them with accurate information so they can work out for themself the difference between fact and fiction.

It may help your child to know:

- Some blood will start to come out of their vagina.
- They may notice a bright red or dark brown stain on their pants or when they wipe after going to the toilet. Or they may feel some unusual wetness between their legs.
- The blood doesn't pour out like water from a tap. It comes out slowly in drips and there may be some chunks in it (tissue from the lining of the uterus).
- Their first couple of periods will usually have a very light blood flow.
- As they become more regular, they may get heavier and last longer.
- They will need to wear a menstrual pad to absorb the blood and to stop it from staining their clothes.
- If they are really paranoid about their period starting without them knowing and showing a stain on their outer clothes, they can wear period underwear (underwear with an inbuilt absorbent lining that won't leak) or a menstrual pad or liner.

Some kids need this extra assurance while they are waiting for their period to start.

How much will they bleed?

It may help your child to know:

- It is different for every person.
- Usually it is about two tablespoons (30 mls or 1 fl oz.).
- Blood often starts off as a rusty color and then gets redder.
- It lightens to a rust color again until it stops.
- The amount of blood can vary from day to day – some days are heavier, and some are lighter.

What is the menstrual cycle?

It may help your child to know:

- Menstrual cycles start from the first day of bleeding until the day before the next bleed.
- When someone has their period, they bleed for a few days, then the bleeding stops.
- They may start to notice some vaginal secretions.
- They ovulate (release an egg).
- Their vaginal secretions will be very slippery like egg white.
- Then there are no secretions.
- They may start to have premenstrual symptoms just before their next period.
- The cycle starts all over again.

How long is the menstrual cycle?

It may help your child to know:

- It is different for every person.
- It can be as short as 21 days or as long as 35 days.
- Periods are often irregular in the beginning because it may take the body a while to adjust to all the changes taking place.
- They may have two periods every month and then nothing for a couple of months. Or it may happen every two-to-three weeks for a cycle or two.
- Sometimes they may even have some spotting of blood for a day or two in the middle of their cycle. This is usually nothing to worry about.
- It can take two-to-three years for their cycle to become regular.

When will they be fertile?

Just because your child has started their period, it doesn't necessarily mean that they're fertile. Ovulation (release of the egg) and menstruation (the shedding of the uterine lining) initially do not always happen together. Some people will ovulate with their first period, but most won't. You will know that your child is ovulating when their menstrual cycle develops a regular pattern. It doesn't really matter whether they're ovulating or not. All your child needs to know is that they are fertile, and pregnancy is possible.

It may help your child to know:

- They will only be fertile for a few days each month.

- During their fertile days, they can become pregnant (if they have sexual intercourse).
- People with a vagina are fertile for a few days each cycle from the first period until they stop at menopause. (Keep things simple and don't confuse them by telling her that they may/ or may not be ovulating at the beginning. At the end of the day, it doesn't really matter. They just need to know that they can now become pregnant.)
- People with a penis are fertile all the time, from the first time they ejaculate and for the rest of their lives. (Keep things simple and don't confuse them by telling them that it usually takes people with a penis a few years to have enough sperm to help make a baby. They just need to know that people with a penis are fertile once they start to ejaculate.)

What is ovulation?

It may help your child to know:

- Ovulation is the periodic release of a mature egg from their ovary.
- This usually happens around the middle of the menstrual cycle.
- Their vaginal secretions will change when they ovulate and become like an egg-white texture.

Could they become pregnant during their period?

It is unlikely, because fertile days are usually around the middle of the menstrual cycle. But, if they have a very short menstrual cycle or bleed for more days than average, it is possible that they could become pregnant during their period.

It may help your child to know:

- It is highly unlikely, but it is possible.
- When they are sexually active, they can then learn more about the signals that the body gives when it is fertile.

What is menopause?

It may help your child to know:

- Menopause is the stage in life when the menstrual cycle stops.
- It ends because the hormones that cause the eggs to mature in the ovaries stop being produced.
- Menopause usually happens when people with a vagina are in their late 40s or early 50s.
- Sometimes it can happen earlier, at around 35, or later, in the late 50s.

How do periods make you feel?

It may help your child to know:

- Sometimes they may feel different around the time of their period.
- It is different for every person – some people feel no different.
- Physical changes may include:

    - Cramps, pain, bloating, weight gain, food cravings, swollen or sore breasts, swollen hands or feet, skin problems, headaches, dizziness, or irritability.
    - Cramps and pain usually don't happen for the first few years of having periods. Some people don't get cramps at all.
- Emotional changes may include:
    - Short temper, aggression, anger, anxiety or panic, confusion, lack of concentration, nervous tension, fatigue, or depression.
- These physical and emotional symptoms are often called premenstrual syndrome or PMS.
- PMS is related to changes in the body's hormones. As hormone levels rise and fall during their menstrual cycle, they can affect the way they feel, both physically and emotionally.
- There are things that they can do to make themself feel better.
- For PMS, they can:
    - Get plenty of exercise.
    - Eat a healthy diet.
    - Get plenty of sleep.
    - Slow down and have some quiet time.
    - Avoid caffeine.
    - Take natural remedies – ask your pharmacist or visit your local health food shop for advice.
- For period pain and cramps, they can:
    - Just put up with it or try to distract themself.
    - Use a hot water bottle or a heat pack on the tummy.
    - Take a hot bath or shower.
    - Try some gentle exercise.

- Drink lots of fluids.
- Ask the local pharmacist about what they recommend for pain relief.

Period celebration

Some families like to celebrate the first period, to acknowledge that their child is on the way to becoming an adult. It can especially help your child to acknowledge that they are leaving their childhood behind. A celebration of their first period is something that you may want to consider in your family. There are lots of different ways that you can do this, but you do need to make sure that it is something that your child is happy about. Listen to what they want to do to celebrate.

Some ideas could include:

- Taking a day off from school and spending it with Mom.
- Going out for dinner as a family.
- Going out for lunch with just your child.
- Buying them flowers, chocolates or a card.
- Writing them a letter and telling them about your hopes and dreams for them.
- Putting together a celebration box filled with things they may need during their period, such as period products, new underwear, a heat pack, essential oils, chocolate, etc.
- Giving them a new journal to write in.
- Planting a tree together in the garden.
- Making them something special, such as a patchwork quilt or a piece of embroidery.

- Giving them tickets to a new play, music concert or movie.
- Having a sleepover with friends.
- Buying a keepsake gift or memento.
- Taking them shopping to buy a new outfit.

You could also look at attending a one-day workshop with your child. *A Celebration Day for Girls* is a one-day workshop for 10-12-years-olds with their mother or a female caregiver. It was designed by Jane Bennett to support girls and mothers at this special threshold in both their lives, and to provide an affirming, grounded and connected celebration of the journey to womanhood. These workshops are offered worldwide, and you can find more information here - Celebration Day for Girls. (http://celebrationdayforgirls.com/)

There are lots of different things that you can do to celebrate with your child. The main thing is that it is something they want to do.

Remember, what matters to your child is the fact that you are acknowledging this transition and that you are spending time just with them.

Period products

There are a lot of different period products out there: pads, tampons, period pants, menstrual cups and sea sponges. You can go natural with reusable cloth products, or you can just buy disposable products at the supermarket. It is pretty much a personal choice as to what your child will want to use.

The easiest thing to start with is pads. Your child needs to be comfortable with inserting their finger into their vagina before they will be ready to use a tampon. Unless your child is a gymnast or a swimmer, keep it simple and start off with pads. You will need to have a supply of pads on hand. There is a wide choice of pads available to use. You can find products that are specifically targeted for tweens or teens. Just look for the packaging that looks brighter or more juvenile or is labeled for 'girls.'

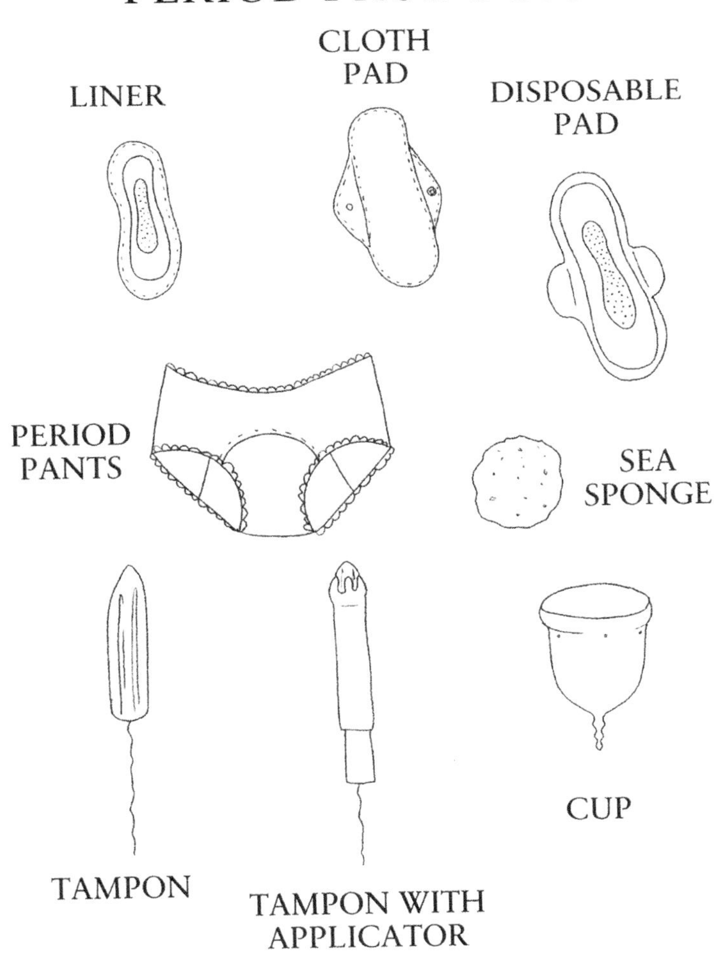

Period starter kits

You can google 'period starter kit' and you will find lots of companies that have free samples they will send to you. This is worth doing as you can then look at the different products and try them before you buy them. It is a good idea to do this early, so your child has more time to get used to these products.

Period kit

A period kit is basically a discreet bag that holds the essentials for having their period. They will then keep it in their schoolbag to use when they have their period.

A period kit can contain:

- Two or three pads.
- Spare underwear in case of leaks.
- Plastic bags to hold stained underpants, or to put used pads in if there isn't a bin handy.
- Cleansing wipes or hand cleanser, just in case they need to clean blood off their hands before leaving the toilet cubicle.

There is a lot more that you can include, but you need to remember that it needs to be small and compact. Kids are easily embarrassed at this age, so they will want something that is discreet rather than too obvious. They don't want one of the other kids to see it and shout, 'Hey, guess who's got their period today!' A pencil case is ideal as it will blend in with their school gear.

If your child is reluctant to have a period kit, remind them that it may come in handy for their friends, too, in case they ever get caught without a pad. A good time to make up a period kit is when your child is 12, or earlier if they have started to show some signs of puberty. It is never too early for a period kit, and it can just disappear into their schoolbag.

A PERIOD KIT

Pad practice

The best way to get your child comfortable with menstrual products is to let them play with them. The best time to do this, of course, is before their first period. But you don't want to start too early. Your child will most likely forget everything you talk about or be overwhelmed by all the information you'll share with them.

Your child is ready for this activity if they have started to grow breasts, has pubic or underarm hair and/or is 12-to-13 years old.

The best way to practice with pads is to find an afternoon together where it is just the two of you. I know that this can sometimes be impossible, especially if you have other kids, but your child will be much more receptive to this activity if they know that it is just the two of you, without the distraction of others.

If you are a dad and don't have a mom available, you can still do this activity. You could find an auntie, a same-sex friend or an older cousin who can chat with your child. It needs to be someone they like and respect. Or you could be upfront with them, acknowledge that you don't know much about this pad thing either, but you're willing to learn, if they are okay with it. You'll need a supply of different menstrual products – pads, liners and tampons. You can buy a selection of different products or order a period starter kit.

Then one afternoon, when it is just the two of you, get them out and play. You could:

- Unpack some pads and compare the sizes and thicknesses of them.

- Explain why you would wear one type of pad over the other.
- Tip some liquid onto the pad and see what happens.
- Peel the paper strip off the pads and apply them to some underwear. Show them how you can place it in their underwear with the sticky side down. Talk about the best style of underwear to wear (firm, not loose fitting).
- Practice sitting on the toilet and putting a pad in. Try showing or explaining how you do it.
- Show them how to roll up a used pad for disposal. Talk about how they can't flush pads down the toilet as it will block the toilet and it could overflow.
- Discuss suitable places for the disposal of used products at home.
- Talk about the special bins that you often find in toilets and explain that they are for this purpose. Discuss what they could do if there isn't a bin next to the toilet. What could they do instead?
- Encourage them to place a pad in their underwear and to walk around with it in place. Let them try the different types so that they can feel the differences between them.
- Try wearing a pad for the whole day, or even the weekend.
- Unwrap some tampons and tell them what they do and where you put them.
- Dip some tampons into water and see how quickly they absorb the liquid.
- Talk about the difference between tampons and pads. When is a good time for them to use a tampon?

- Share your own stories with your child – your first period, the products that you used, inserting your first tampon, how you felt, etc. Stories are important and your child will enjoy them.
- Discuss what they could do if they are out and don't have a pad. Who could they ask, especially if they are at school? Show them how to fold up toilet paper to make up a temporary pad.
- Talk about how often they should change their pad, and how they can tell when it is due for a change. Let them know that it is normal for some blood to leak onto their underpants or sheets at night.
- Discuss where you will store products for them to use. Will they tell you if they run out?
- Make up a period kit together and encourage them to keep it in their schoolbag.
- Talk about the importance of having clean hands when using pads, both before and after.

And don't forget to have fun. This doesn't have to be a formal teaching session. It is an opportunity for you to show your child that you are an expert and that they can come to you for advice.

Penis

Your child needs to know that their penis will be changing too. As well as growing bigger, erections will be much more frequent, and they will begin to ejaculate.

It may help your child to know that:

- Their penis will grow longer before it grows wider.
- Penises come in all shapes, sizes and colors. Some are long, some are short. Some are wide and some are narrow. It is unique, just like your face is unique to you.
- Bigger penises are not always better. Sex is about more than the size of your penis.

Pearly penile papules

All penises are different, and it is normal for some penises to have pearly penile papules. These are little flesh-colored bumps that form a ring around the base of the glans, the 'head' of the penis. They are all about the same size and shape and they do not bleed, itch, or hurt.

It may help your child to know that:

- Every penis is different.
- Some penises can have pearly penile papules. These are little bumps under the head of the penis.
- They are more common in boys with a foreskin but can still be found on circumcised penises.
- Sometimes they can be mistaken for warts.
- Some people may not know they have them until a sexual partner tells them. Some people don't notice them until they are adults.
- They are perfectly normal and are a healthy variation. They do not need to be removed.
- Most kids (and adults) worry when they first find them.

PEARLY PENILE PAPULES

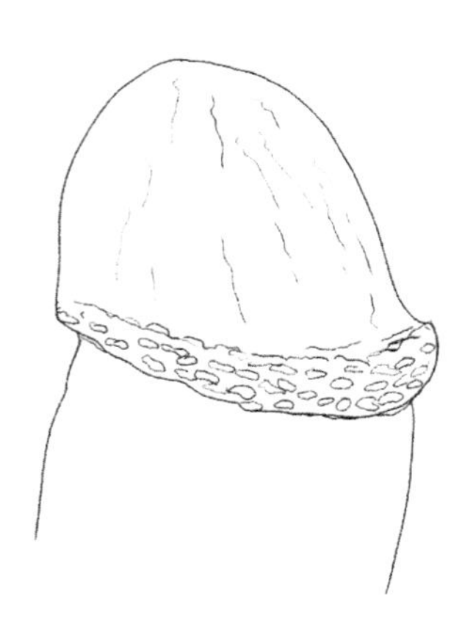

Foreskin

Your child needs to know that as they go through puberty, their foreskin will become easier to retract (pull back) and they will need to start cleaning under their foreskin as part of their daily routine.

Don't be alarmed if your child's foreskin isn't retractable or only partially retracts. At birth, the foreskin is attached to the glans (head of the penis) and has a tight opening at the end. Which means it isn't retractable, i.e., the foreskin can't be pulled back to expose the glans. As your child grows older, and plays with their penis, the foreskin will gradually separate from the head of the penis and become retractable. Which means that full retraction is possible in 50% of 10-year-olds and 99% of 17-year-olds. [1]

Teach your child to clean their foreskin in the following way:

1. Gently pull the foreskin back away from the end of the penis.

2. Rinse underneath the foreskin with a mild or unscented soap and warm water. (Some people choose to not use soap, so it's up to you as to whether you do or don't.)
3. Make sure the soap is properly rinsed away and that none is left on the skin.
4. Pull the foreskin back over the penis.

It may help your child to know:

- The foreskin is there to protect the head of the penis.
- As they get older, their foreskin will slowly loosen up and they will be able to pull it back so they can see the head of their penis.
- They should never forcibly retract their foreskin back. If it hurts, they should stop what they are doing.
- The foreskin should always be pulled back into its natural position after retracting. If they can't pull it back, they need to let you know as there is a chance they will permanently damage their penis. This is called Paraphimosis and you will need to seek urgent medical attention.
- When washing, it is important to not use too much soap and to ensure that soap is properly rinsed away. Otherwise, the skin underneath may become irritated and sore.
- Some people don't use soap at all. They may find that soap irritates or dries their skin. Whether to use soap or not is up to you.
- Smegma (the white discharge found under their foreskin) is normal but needs to be washed away every 1 to 3 days (more often if it becomes smelly or there is more than usual).

- Every foreskin is different. Some are longer or shorter than others.
- If they don't clean under their foreskin regularly, then there's a risk of infection (which means a trip to the doctor).

You can read more about penis and foreskin care in this article - https://sexedrescue.com/penis-care/

1 Clinical Practice Guidelines: The penis and foreskin. The Royal Children's Hospital Melbourne. July 2018. Retrieved 29 July 2020 https://www.rch.org.au/clinicalguide/guideline_index/The_penis_and_foreskin/

Circumcision

Your child needs to know that some penises look different for a reason. Some kids will have a circumcised penis, where the foreskin, or skin at the end of the penis, is removed.

It may help your child to know that:

- Some kids will have a different-looking penis because they have been circumcised.
- Circumcision is a medical procedure where the foreskin, the skin at the end of the penis, is removed.
- It can happen for cultural or religious reasons. It can also happen for medical reasons, when the foreskin is too tight to be pulled back (retracted).
- Some people are circumcised when they are infants, children or even adults.

- A circumcised penis still works the same way. They will still have erections and ejaculate.

CIRCUMCISION

BEFORE AFTER

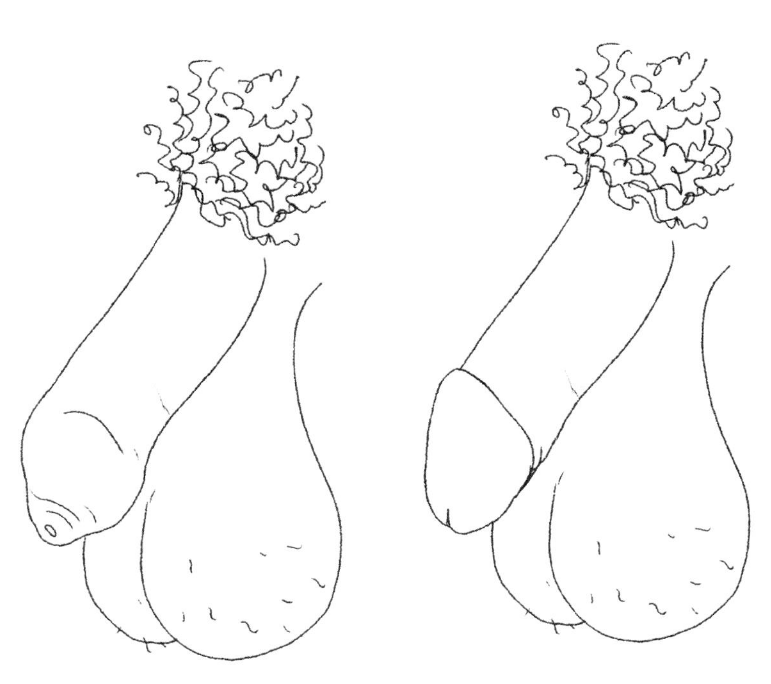

Testicles

One of the first physical changes that will happen to your child with a penis during puberty will be to their testicles. Over the next few years, they will slowly start increasing in size as they develop the parts necessary to make sperm.

It may help your child to know that:

- Their testicles will start to grow bigger and to hang lower.
- They can range in size from big to small. Bigger does not mean better.
- Their testicles are very sensitive. In some sports, they may need to wear a box or jock strap to protect them from being damaged.
- Testicles have two jobs to do – to make sperm and to make androgens (the male hormones).
- The skin on their scrotum will start to change and become thinner, redder, pimply/bumpy.
- Their scrotum can shrink when cold or if swimming in cold water and stretch when warm, like after a hot bath.
- Testicles like to stay at a constant temperature, around two-to-four degrees cooler than normal body temperature. This is why they move around in the scrotum.
- In late puberty, they need to start checking their testicles for signs of testicular cancer, such as lumps or bumps. Once a month, they should roll their testicle between their thumb and three fingers when in a hot shower or bath. The testicle should feel soft and smooth like a boiled egg that has been peeled.

Erections

Your child needs to know that they will start having more erections as they go through puberty. This is a normal part of puberty and it happens to all people with a penis.

It may help your child to know that:

- An erection is when their penis becomes stiff and hard, larger and longer, and stands out from the body.
- They have been having erections since they were a baby, but they will now happen a lot more.
- There are lots of different slang terms for erections, such as 'boner' and 'hard on.'
- Their penis can feel hard as if there is a bone inside, but there isn't. There is lots of spongy tissue instead, which gets hard when it is filled with blood.
- Erections can happen slowly or very quickly.
- Some kids worry about the size of their penis. Usually, there is nothing to worry about, and it will be the right size penis for them. Penises shown on porn videos are not normal and are chosen because they are unusually large.
- Their penis will always look smaller when they are looking down at it. Tell them to try standing in front of a mirror, and they will see the difference.
- They don't have to ejaculate just because their penis is erect.
- Pre-ejaculatory fluid, or pre-cum, is a small amount of clear liquid that comes out of the penis when sexually aroused.
- An erect penis can stick out at different angles, or it may stand nearly straight up. When erect, it may be straight, curve to the right or the left, or some other way. No matter what the angle is, it's perfectly normal.
- Everyone's penis is different.

Unwanted erections

It may help your child to know that erections can happen for lots of different reasons. They might have a full bladder, their clothes might be rubbing against their penis, or they might be having some sexy thoughts. They can also happen for no reason at all. This can be embarrassing, and your child may need to be reminded that all kids (and adults) have unwanted erections. As their hormones settle, they won't happen as often.

Some tips for managing unwanted erections:

- Wear baggy pants and long shirts if they keep on happening.
- Hold schoolbooks or a bag in front of an erection.
- Sit down when having an erection.
- Put hands in pockets to try and hide it.
- Tie a jumper/shirt around the waist and let the sleeves cover it.
- Try to focus on something else until it goes away.
- Remember, it is more noticeable to the person having the erection than to anyone else!

Ejaculation

Early in puberty, your child will start to make sperm. It takes a few years though until their body is ready for ejaculation. This usually happens when people with a penis are aged 13 to 14, sometimes older, or even younger, and nearly always through masturbation or by having a wet dream.

It may help your child to know that:

- One day, some fluid will come out of the hole at the end of their penis.
- This only happens when their penis is erect. It can happen when masturbating, during sex and during a wet dream.
- They need to be having sexy thoughts and to be sexually aroused for ejaculation to happen. It won't just happen because they have an erection.
- This is something that happens to all people with a penis and will happen for the rest of their life.
- This fluid is called semen, and it contains their sperm. Sperm is needed to help make a baby:
    - About one teaspoon of white, creamy semen is ejaculated, sometimes less (1/2 tsp) or more (2 tsp).
    - Semen comes out in five-or-six spurts, sometimes more or less. It is more likely to dribble out in kids rather than spurt.
- Semen is different from pre-ejaculatory fluid (or pre-cum), which is a small amount of clear liquid that comes out of the penis when sexually aroused.
- Once they start to ejaculate, they are fertile, which means that they could make a baby and become a parent.

Sexual feelings

During puberty, your child will experience sexual feelings for the first time in their life. The hormones that are busy making their body fertile are also making sure that they'll want to have sex so that they can make a baby, which means that they will start to have sexual thoughts and be sexually attracted to others.

It may help your child to know:

- During puberty, it is normal to become attracted to the opposite and/or same sex, and to feel more sexual.
- It is also normal to not experience sexual feelings. Asexuality is when someone is uninterested in sex or feels no desire for sex.
- Some kids will experience stronger or weaker sexual feelings than others. Some kids will start to have sexual feelings sooner or later than others. Everyone is different.
- In people with a vagina, the main physical sign of sexual excitement is wetness of the vagina.
- In people with a penis, it is to have an erect penis.
- Sexual feelings can come from reading a romantic novel, watching a movie, or thinking about another person in a romantic way.
- Having sexual feelings is normal and is nothing to feel guilty about.
- Acting on such feelings with a partner is a big responsibility, and it is best to wait until older.

Wet dreams

People with a penis

During puberty, kids with a penis will start to have wet dreams, or nocturnal emissions. Not all people with a penis have wet dreams, but it is better that your child know that they are normal, than to worry that there is something wrong with their penis.

It may help your child to know that:

- They might experience something called a wet dream.
- A wet dream happens when they are asleep.
- The penis becomes erect and ejaculates while they are sleeping. They might wake up just as they are about to ejaculate, as they are ejaculating, or just after ejaculation.
- They might not wake up at all. This means that they may wake up with a wet patch in their pajama pants or in their bed.
- Sometimes, the semen has dried up before waking, and they may just find a slight watermark.
- Wet dreams are normal and natural.
- They can't stop themself from having wet dreams.
- Not all people with a penis have them; it is normal whether they do or don't.
- Some kids find them embarrassing, and that's okay.
- They can start changing their own sheets, or doing their own washing, if they aren't comfortable with anyone knowing about it.

People with a vagina

Kids with a vagina can have wet dreams as well. They'll have a sexual dream where their vagina lubricates and they may orgasm. They may wake up during them or they may not. They are seen as a normal part of growing up, and some kids will have them, whereas others won't. They shouldn't worry about whether they have them or not.

Masturbation

During puberty, your child might discover that touching or rubbing their genitals can feel nice.

For kids with a vagina, their vagina may become wet, moist, or tingly from self-stimulation, and they may experience orgasm.

For kids with a penis, their penis will become erect, they'll ejaculate and experience orgasm.

An orgasm is a really nice feeling that can sometimes happen during masturbation or sexual activity. It is not easy to explain how an orgasm feels, because it can be different each time. You could describe it as a really nice feeling that starts in the genitals and can also be felt throughout the whole body. This feeling then begins to feel stronger and stronger, building up until you begin to feel waves of intense feelings.

Masturbation is not harmful as long as it is kept private. There is no scientific evidence that it causes any harm to the body or mind. It is only a problem when it stops you from doing other things, or when it is done in public. However, there are many religious and cultural beliefs around masturbation.

It may help your child to know:

- Masturbation is often the first way people can experience sexual pleasure.

- Many kids begin to masturbate for sexual pleasure during puberty.
- Some kids never masturbate. This is normal too.
- Masturbation does not cause physical or mental harm.
- Some cultures and religions oppose masturbation (talk to your religious leader).
- The decision about whether or not to masturbate is a personal one.
- Masturbation is a private activity.
- Many adults masturbate at some time in their lives.

Conception

Puberty happens for one reason – reproduction. This is so your child can make a baby and start the next generation. They need to know that this can happen and how it happens.

It may help your child to know:

- A baby is made when an egg from a female joins with sperm from a male.
- This can happen during sexual intercourse, when the penis is inside the vagina.
- Their bodies move together and after a short time, semen containing sperm comes out of the penis.
- The sperm travels up through the uterus and into the fallopian tubes. If one strong sperm joins with an egg, a baby begins to form.
- Babies can also be made with medical assistance, such as in vitro fertilization (IVF) or surrogacy.

Sex

Talking about puberty means also talking about sex. As puberty progresses, your child is going to start thinking of sex differently. Before puberty, they only thought of sex in a theoretical way, as something adults do. Now, as their hormones rewire them to reproduce, they will start to think of sex as something that they will want to do. This means you need to start talking to your child about sex. If you have never talked about sex with them before, don't expect them to be totally ignorant. It is very possible that they will have heard other kids talk about sex or have read about it.

When talking to your child, it is important to remember that sex is more than the type of sexual activity that makes a baby. It can include oral sex, anal sex, and lots of touching where no penetration happens at all. Sex can also happen in lots of different ways. It might happen between two people who are in a loving and committed relationship, but it can also happen between two people who have only just met. Your child will hear a lot of mixed negative messages about sex and may need some help trying to interpret them.

When talking about sex, there are two parts to the conversation. First, it is about giving your child information, or the facts: for example, sex can be when the female lets the male put their penis inside their vagina. Second, it is about providing them with some guidelines about what is appropriate behavior: for example, you think they should wait until they are married, or in a loving, committed relationship, before they have sexual intercourse.

It is important that you share your sexual attitudes and behaviors with your child. And don't just tell them what they are. You need to explain why you feel this way, so your child can understand. Knowing the 'why' will help them while they are forming their own sexual values.

It may help your child to know:

- Sex can be lots of different things, but when you hear people talking about it, they are usually referring to sexual intercourse.
- Adults have sex for lots of different reasons:
    - To make a baby.
    - It feels good (it can also feel awful).
    - For fun.
    - It is a way to show love or to get close to someone.
- Sex is something that is just for adults. It isn't for kids and it isn't something that you should do with members of your family.
- Sex is something that is private and should only happen when ... (share your beliefs about when it is okay for them to think about sex).
- Sex is special and is something that should happen with someone that you trust and care deeply about.

Consent

This is the age where you need to talk about consent in more detail. For the first time, your child is starting to explore what sex means. As you start to talk about sex, you also need to talk about consent for sex. Learning about consent will take many conversations.

It may help your child to know:

- Consent is when you agree to do something, or you allow something to happen to you.
- In some situations, it isn't possible to give consent, such as when under the influence of drugs or alcohol.
- How to give or withhold consent and ask for it from others.
- How to seek help when they, or someone else, is having their right to consent violated.
- The consequences of not respecting consent, such as sexual assault, rape, or sex with a minor.
- Consent can be partial, for example, it is okay to do this but not this. 'You can kiss me, but don't put your hands down my shirt.'
- It is okay to change your mind later on: for example, you can withdraw consent at any time.

Sexual attraction

During puberty, your child will discover whether they are attracted to the opposite sex and/or the same sex. Some kids will already know this, but some won't have given it much thought until now. One in every 10 people will be attracted to people of the same sex. So, it is possible that your child will be same-sex attracted. Who your child is attracted to is not their choice. They can't choose to like the opposite sex instead. It just isn't possible. They can try, but it won't work.

By now, they'll have already worked out that most people like the opposite sex (people with a penis are attracted to people with a vagina and vice versa). It is what they see on TV, read about in books and see around them. They will have also heard negative comments being made about being 'gay' and will have picked up on the fact that it isn't something that society as a whole is supportive about. Which means that for same-sex attracted kids, this can be a confusing time in which they will need your support. Whether you believe that same-sex attraction is okay or not okay, you still need to talk to your child about the fact that some kids are attracted to the same sex and sometimes even both sexes. All children need to know that sexual orientation is not a choice, that all people deserve respect regardless of their sexual orientation, and that who we are attracted to, whether it be someone with a penis or vagina, is only a small part of who we are.

Just remember to discuss this topic with care and sensitivity, regardless of your beliefs. Sexual attraction is not a choice. If your child ends up being attracted to the same sex, how will they feel about it and will they feel safe talking to you about it?

It may help your child to know:

- Puberty is the time we usually discover which sex (or sexes) we are attracted to.
- They may feel attracted to the opposite or same sex. They may feel attracted to both sexes, or they may not feel attracted to anyone. This is all normal.
- They will either like people with a penis or people with a vagina, both or none. In time, they will know who they like.
- They cannot change who they are attracted to.
- All people deserve respect regardless of their sexual orientation.

- Who they are attracted to, someone with a penis and/or vagina, is only a small part of who they are.
- They need to know about homophobia, and that some religions and cultures believe that same-sex attraction (homosexuality) is wrong.

Preventing pregnancy

Your child won't need a lot of information about contraception until they are showing an interest in romantic relationships. You can give them the information, but it won't really be relevant until they are thinking about being sexually active. But they still need to know that pregnancy can be prevented.

It may help your child to know:

- When 2 people want to have sexual intercourse without having a child, they can use a family planning method to prevent pregnancy.
- There are many types of family planning methods, also called contraceptives:
    - Abstinence, condom, implants, pill, injections, morning after pill.
- A person with a vagina cannot become pregnant if they have sex with another person with a vagina.
- A person with a penis cannot become pregnant if they have sex with another person with a penis.
- Unprotected sex means having sexual intercourse without any contraception.
- Some religions and cultures are against the use of contraception.

Sexually transmitted infections (STIs)

Your child won't need a lot of information about STIs until they are showing an interest in romantic relationships. You can give them the information, but it won't really be relevant until they are thinking about being sexually active. They still need to know that there are infections that can be spread through sexual contact.

It may help your child to know:

- STIs are spread through sexual contact, which includes sexual intercourse and anal or oral contact. Some examples of STIs are:
    - Syphilis, gonorrhea, chlamydia, genital herpes, trichomoniasis, hepatitis B, human papilloma virus (HPV), and HIV.
- They can protect themself by using condoms and not having sexual contact with an infected person.
- STIs aren't nice things to have:
    - The symptoms for people with a vagina can include genital sores or ulcers, lower abdominal pain or tenderness, unusual vaginal discharge, vaginal itching, painful urination, or painful sexual intercourse, depending on the STI.
    - The symptoms for people with a penis can include painful urination, urethral discharge, ulcers, or sores, depending on the STI.
- STIs need to be treated with medication or they can cause serious problems.

- Some STIs cause permanent infertility, chronic pain, and cancer of the cervix. Without treatment, heart and brain damage can develop 10-to-25 years after initial exposure to syphilis.
- Sex is not free of risks.

Online safety

As your child goes through puberty, they will become more curious about sex. They will also become more independent and not always come to you with their questions. Instead, they will head to the next best thing – the internet – to search for answers. They are going to stumble across sexually-explicit content – in the form of pornography – in their search for knowledge. They will also find information that looks reliable but isn't.

It may help your child to know:

- What your family rules are regarding the safe use of internet-enabled devices, as well as the consequences if they break these rules.
- Sometimes it is hard to tell if information on the internet is reliable or not.
- They will stumble across sexually explicit images online (if they haven't already). If they do, they should turn off the device and inform an adult they trust. Remind them that they won't get into trouble.
- Porn is not the best way to learn about sex. If they have any questions, they can ask you or find the answer in an age-appropriate book or website.

- Sending and receiving naked photos of private parts is illegal, until they are legally deemed an adult. The age varies in different countries, but it is usually 16.

You can access my FREE sex education course for parents at https://sexedrescue.com/back-to-basics/

HOW DO I START TALKING ABOUT PUBERTY?

It isn't what you say that matters. What matters is that you're giving your child the message that you're open to talking to them about anything' no matter what.

Getting started

The hardest part of talking to kids about puberty is getting started. You know what you can talk about, but how do you actually say it? How do you start the conversation?

It is normal to feel a little uncomfortable when you first start talking about puberty with your child. We all do. Many of us didn't have comfortable conversations with our own parents when growing up. We don't have any helpful memories of what to do, just lots of memories of what not to do! Like with all new things, it will get easier. The more often you talk with your child about puberty, the easier it will get.

You'll find many suggestions on different ways to start talking with your child about puberty. Try to pick just one to start with, rather than trying to do them all. Choose one that feels comfortable, or like something you may already be doing. For example, if you already buy books for your child, buying a book on puberty is a great way to start.

Key messages

So, what are the main messages that you need to give your child?

- They aren't alone!
- You've been through puberty too, so you do understand what it may be like for them.
- They can talk to you about anything, no matter what.
- You will answer their questions truthfully.
- If you don't know the answer, you will find it and get back to them with it.
- What sexual attitudes and behaviors are okay, and not okay, in your family.
- They are normal!

At the end of the day, it isn't about how much information you share. It is about the fact that you are talking openly about growing up. This means that you will have an open relationship where your child can talk to you about anything, no matter what. As a parent, that is pretty much what we all want.

Everyday approach

The best approach with talking is to keep it as much like an everyday conversation as possible. If your child can sense a lecture coming on, they will tune out and stop listening almost immediately. Make sure you use an everyday tone and language. Try to talk about periods in the same voice and way that you would use when talking about their plans for the weekend. By sounding everyday (or natural), you are letting them know what is happening to them is normal and nothing to be ashamed of.

Get ready to repeat yourself, as you will need to have many conversations on the one topic before they will fully understand (and remember) what you've been saying. This is completely normal and is the way their brain works. Try to tell them a little bit more than you think they need to know. As parents, we automatically tend to err on the side of caution and tell our kids less than they need to know, especially when it comes to love, sex and relationships.

Don't assume that they are too young or not ready for it. If they aren't ready, they'll just forget whatever it is that you said. When they are ready for that bit of information, they'll probably let you know.

Don't forget to listen, too. Listen to what they have to say, or what they think. They probably know a lot more than you think they do.

When starting late

If you've never talked about any of this stuff before, it isn't too late to start, even if your child already has hair in new places.

So, what's the best way to get started, when starting late?

First, you need to warn your child that you are going to start talking about puberty and growing up. You could try explaining that you've realized that you haven't talked about puberty before, but that you would like to change that.

You could try saying:

- *A book I'm reading is about puberty. I know we haven't really talked about puberty before, but I'm going to try to change that, so we can have conversations about it.*
- *A book I'm reading made me realize how important it is for parents to talk with their kids about puberty. Since we haven't talked about it before, I'd like to start.*

Second, explain why you haven't talked to them about puberty and growing up before.

You could try saying:

- *It's something that my parents didn't talk about very much when I was a kid.*
- *I've always been worried that I would be bringing it up at the wrong time or the wrong place.*
- *I've always worried that I would get it all wrong or do as bad a job as my parents did.*
- *I've always been worried about saying too much or too little or even saying the wrong thing.*
- *Talking about sex makes me feel really uncomfortable.*

Third, explain what is going to change.

You could try saying:

- *I want us to be able to talk about anything, including sex. You are going to hear me talking about puberty and growing up. If you have any questions or want to talk about something, I want you to know that I am always available.*

Getting past your fears and worries

A lot of parents wonder if they are doing the right thing.

Maybe your child is too young for all this? Maybe or maybe not. Puberty happens whether kids are emotionally ready for it or not. Isn't it better that your child is prepared for the changes that will soon be happening to them, and for them to know that they can turn to you for support, guidance and information?

Won't you be encouraging them to be sexual? No, not at all. All you're doing is giving them information about what will be happening to them. You're also guiding them, because you're telling them what sexual behavior and attitudes are okay, and not okay, in your family. Research tells us that kids who have received good sex education are less likely to be sexually active and when they are, they will be much safer than their uneducated peers.[1]

They haven't asked any questions yet, so maybe they aren't interested? Some kids ask questions, and some don't. But it doesn't

[1] SRE – the evidence. 2015. Evidence briefing. Sex Education Forum http://www.sexeducationforum.org.uk/evidence.aspx

mean that they aren't interested. It just means that you will have to be the first one to bring it up.

Maybe you will say too much, or not enough? Or even the wrong thing? Possibly, but it doesn't really matter if you do. What matters is that you are showing your child that you are willing to talk to them about puberty, love, sex and relationships. You are letting them know that they can come and talk to you about anything. That's what really matters.

Getting comfortable if you haven't talked about this stuff before

It is normal for both parents and kids to feel uncomfortable talking about puberty. Luckily for you, it does get easier the more you do it.

There are some things that you can do to help manage embarrassment:

- Let your child know if you sense that they are uncomfortable talking about puberty. Try saying:
    - *Some kids can feel really uncomfortable talking about puberty with their parents. I totally get it! I feel awkward talking about it too. Maybe we can help each other get past the awkwardness*
- Let your child know that you feel embarrassed. Try saying something like:
    - *I feel a bit uncomfortable talking about puberty because my parents never talked with me about it. But this is an important subject, so I really want to talk with you about it.*
- Keep it simple and talk about one topic at a time. Decide what you want to talk about, such as the need to wear deodorant

to manage body odor. Spend a moment and think about the best way to casually bring up the topic. You might say:
  - *Hey, I bought this for you at the supermarket today* (show them the deodorant). *Now that you're going through puberty, you'll sweat more and stink! This will help you to stink less. You just spray it onto each underarm. Just like this* (apply deodorant to yourself). *Does that make sense?*
- Talk when you're doing something else, such as washing dishes; this makes it seem like an everyday topic and not something to be ashamed of.
- Take a deep breath and take your time to respond to questions. There is no rush!
- Use humor. You don't have to make a joke about it but laughing about puberty shows that it is a normal topic.
- Get some puberty books to read with your child. This way you don't have to stress about remembering what to say, as all the information is there in the book.

Sharing values

Don't forget to also talk about your sexual attitudes and beliefs. Don't just talk about the fact that you can prevent pregnancies with contraception. Share with your child what your thoughts are about contraception and unplanned pregnancy. Explain the reasons behind your belief so that your child understands why.

Don't just tell your child what sex is all about. Also let them know when you think it is a good time for them to think about sex. It might not be until they are married, or of legal age, or they should be in a loving, committed relationship first. Again, explain why, so that your child can understand the reasoning behind your beliefs.

Try to get into the habit of explaining what you think or believe when talking about love, sex and relationships. This is your opportunity to guide your child as they grow up, and to help them make healthy decisions around love, sex and relationships.

Share stories

Most kids are interested in hearing their parents' stories about growing up. Try to remember what it was like yourself, going through puberty. How did you feel? Who did you talk to? What were your fears? Sharing stories about what puberty was like for you reassures your child that you do know what they are going through. Plus, it is a great way to build connection and trust with your child.

Try saying things like:

- *I remember when I found my first pubic hair. I didn't know I would get hair down there, so I found some scissors and cut it off.*
- *I remember my first kiss. I really liked this person and one weekend at a party, we found a dark corner and kissed. All I really remember is this cold wet tongue being poked into my mouth, lots!*
- *I remember when I first started to like boys. I used to think about them all the time and daydream about being their girlfriend.*
- *I remember when my first period started. I was too embarrassed to say something to my mother. Right up until I left home, I used to sneak into her bedroom when she wasn't home and take one or two pads at a time.*

- *I asked your dad what he used to do when he was a boy and had wet dreams. He said that he used to wipe himself clean with an old shirt and then throw it into the bottom of the wash basket. It was something that he felt really embarrassed about and it was something that his parents never talked about.*

Take it slow

When talking to kids about puberty, there is no rush. Today, we know that the best way for kids to learn is through lots of frequent, repetitive conversations. If your child looks like they aren't listening, don't despair. They probably are listening but hiding their discomfort by pretending not to. Keep on talking regardless. Just make sure you keep it conversational; don't turn it into a lecture and don't overdo it. Maybe keep it to one or two comments a week.

By keeping the conversation open, you are letting them know that they can come and talk to you about anything.

Be available

By talking to your child about puberty and growing up, you are letting them know that you are available and willing to talk. Make sure you tell them that they can come to you with any questions or concerns at any time. Don't be too pushy or obvious. You've got plenty of time to talk about all this stuff – there is no rush. If they throw you an opportunity to talk, make sure you grab it and talk. Yes, life does get busy, but five or 10 minutes of your time is often all that they need.

Try to encourage them to talk about how they feel about growing up and changing. Ask them what they're looking forward to and what they're nervous about.

Normalize it

It is really important to normalize puberty for your child. They need to know that what is happening to them is completely normal, and it is happening to their friends too.

It may help your child to know:

- Everyone is different.
- Some kids start early, some start late.
- Some kids develop fast, some develop slowly.
- Sometimes it can feel out of control.
- Going through puberty can be hard:
    - Your emotions swing.
    - Your body changes.
    - You start to have sexual feelings.
    - Your relationships with family and friends begin to change.
- Their body is doing what it is meant to do.

Third person

Talking in the third person can sometimes make it a bit less uncomfortable, for both you and your child.

You could try saying:

- *I saw your friend Amy the other day and noticed that they're starting to grow breasts. It made me think that maybe we should be starting to talk about bras and things for when you start developing.*
- *One of the mums was talking today about how their daughter has started their period. It made me realize that we haven't really started to chat yet about periods.*
- *I heard a story on the radio today, where an expert was talking about how many kids don't understand what puberty is. Have any of your friends talked about puberty yet, or about any of the changes that are happening to them?*

Books

Books make talking about puberty a lot easier. There are a lot of puberty books that have been written specifically for kids. They'll provide your child with all the information they need to know. You don't have to worry about trying to remember everything. Plus, the information in books is usually accurate, reliable, and written age-appropriately in language that kids will understand.

Many of the books are sorted into genders (boys and girls) with some being for all kids.

Some books are written for younger kids and will only talk about puberty and the changes that will happen. These books don't talk about sex, mainly because they target a younger audience, such as eight-to-11-year-olds. There are also books that talk about puberty and growing up. Growing up always includes topics like love, sex, relationships, contraception, etc. These topics are always talked about in an age-appropriate way and are what 12-to-14-year-olds are curious about.

Choosing the right book comes down to a number of things, such as the age of your child, their level of reading and how much information you are happy letting them have. If they are young, you'll want a book that won't overwhelm with too much detailed information or talk about sex. You can get them a more detailed book later on.

Your instinct may be to go with a book that doesn't talk about love, sex and relationships. If they are really young (eight-10), or quite immature compared to their peers, that's fine. But do remember that you aren't protecting them by withholding information. If anything, you are leaving your child vulnerable, as they will just turn to their peers or the internet instead.

You can read the book together, or your child can have it to read alone. If they are reading it alone, just make sure that they know that they can come to you with any questions.

You could try saying:

- *I heard about this great book on puberty, so I bought a copy of it. We can read it together if you like.*
- *You've now reached an age where your body is going to start changing from being a kid to a grownup. I've bought a book that we can read together that talks about what will happen and why. How about we start reading it together tonight?*

- *Jo's mum told me about a book on puberty that she bought for them to read. I bought you a copy to read by yourself, if you like. If you want to talk about anything in it with me, that would be great.*

To talk about the book later, you could try saying:

- *Remember how we read that book about puberty? Well, I was wondering if you had any questions?*
- *Remember that puberty book I bought you? Does it talk about wet dreams (or periods)?*

To choose a puberty book, you can visit your local library or bookshop. You will find a lot of puberty books listed and reviewed on this book review site: http://sexedrescue.com/sex-education-books-for-children/

Teachable moments

An easy way to provide information to your child is to find an everyday situation and turn it into an opportunity to teach something. At first you might find them a little bit hard to find. So, try thinking of one topic, for example, pornography, and start looking for opportunities to chat about porn. It could be a story on the radio, an article in the newspaper, a post that you found on Facebook, a blogpost, or something you read in a book. Once you start looking, you will find opportunities for talking, and teachable moments, everywhere.

Some opportunities for teachable moments could include:

- *Did you hear that story on the news about those teenagers sharing videos of a drunk girl being raped? They are probably going to end up with a prison sentence for it. What do you think you would do if you were at a party and you saw your friends doing something like that? What could you do?*
- *See those two girls over there on the bench? The ones holding hands and kissing? How hard do you think it was for them to tell their family and friends that they were gay?*
- *Look at this magazine ad. Do you think that all people have bodies like that?*
- *Wow, did you hear the words to that song? It was about oral sex. They say that oral sex is something that teens often do with their first kiss. What do you think of that?*
- (Referring to a TV show or movie that you're both watching together:) *Do you think that it's okay to have sex with someone you have only just met?*
- *Can you put these tampons away for me in my bathroom? I guess that we should probably start talking about when you will get your first period. What do you think?*
- *Did you see what the ad on TV was about? It was talking about hair removal. You're going to start getting hair in some new places soon.*

Pre-warn them

If you want to talk about a particular topic, for example, periods, let your child know in advance. It pre-warns them and can sometimes make them more receptive to talking.

You could try saying:

- *I want to talk to you this weekend about the different products that you can use for periods. It will be just you and me, with no other kids.*
- *I bought a puberty book for you today. I thought we could start reading it together before you go to bed tonight.*
- *Hey, I want to talk to you tonight about a sex/puberty thing. Don't worry, you're not in trouble or anything. I just want to talk.*

Answering questions

If your child is old enough to ask the question, then they're usually old enough for the answer. Which means that the best approach to answering their questions is openly and honestly.

It is important to try to answer their question as if it is one of the many other questions that they ask each day. This way they won't see the topic as being shameful.

Keep your answers brief, factual and positive (irrespective of your child's age). If they want more information, they will usually ask for it. You can even ask them if that answered their question or if they need more information.

Try asking your child what they think before answering. You could try saying, 'What made you think of that?' This will then give you a little time to think of an answer and to work out what your child already knows.

If you're unsure about the meaning of their question, check in with them. For example, 'Do you mean how do babies grow when they are inside their mother? Or how do two people start a baby growing?'

And remember, it may feel awkward when your first start but the more you talk, the easier it gets!

In Chapter 7, you'll find simple explanations for some of the most common questions kids ask parents about puberty and sex.

When you don't know the answer

Your child will ask you questions to which you don't know the answer. No one knows everything and I can guarantee that they are already asking you questions you don't have the answer for. The best way to manage this is to be completely honest and say, 'I don't know.' Then tell them that you'll find out and get back to them with an answer. If the topic isn't too risqué, you could both go and google it, or look it up in a book together. Just be careful when googling topics about puberty and sex, as you will often find pornography or content that isn't age-appropriate. Whatever you do, don't forget to get back to them with the answer. Forgetting could signal to your child that you aren't reliable, that the topic is taboo, or that you aren't comfortable answering these types of questions. This means that they'll start to look elsewhere for answers, which isn't a good thing.

Delaying answers

Sometimes, we just can't answer questions straight away. Your child may have asked you a question at the wrong time or the wrong place, or maybe you are just too busy or too uncomfortable to answer it on the spot. It is helpful if you can have your standard response to untimely questions worked out in advance. Acknowledge that they asked a question and explain when you'll respond.

You could try saying:

- *That's a great question, but how about we talk about that when we get home?*
- *I'm not sure about that. How about we talk about that later when I'm not so busy?*
- *You know what, I don't know. How about I find out the answer and I get back to you with it?*

If you get forgetful, send yourself an email, or post a note somewhere to remember. When you find the answer, you can restart the conversation with something as simple as, 'Remember how you asked me about periods earlier today? Well, I found the answer to your question.'

Check you've given them enough information

Make sure you check back with your child and confirm that you have understood their question and that you've given them enough information.

You could try saying:

- *Did that answer your question?*
- *Does that make sense?*
- *Was there anything else you wanted to know?*
- *Do you have any more questions?*

Answering personal questions

Your child may ask you some personal questions about puberty and sex that you won't feel comfortable answering. They might ask you about your first period, or about the first time you had sex. If the question is too personal, you don't need to answer it. See it as an opportunity to reinforce privacy but also try to turn it into an educational opportunity.

You could try saying:

- *That is a personal question that I'm not comfortable answering. But I know that it is illegal for children to have sex until they are 16.*
- *Some stuff is private and personal, so I don't really want to answer that question. But I know that they talk about that in your puberty book, so let's go and see what it has to say about it.*

You can access my FREE sex education course for parents at https://sexedrescue.com/back-to-basics/

QUESTIONS & ANSWERS

Answering your child's questions about puberty can be tricky. You might be worried that you'll say too much. Or even worse...not enough.

So, here are some 1-3 sentence explanations that give your child the right amount of information in an age-appropriate way. Explanations that they'll understand and will make perfect sense to them.

The Basics

What is puberty?

Puberty is when your body changes from being a child to a grown-up.

Why does puberty happen?

To get your body ready so that you can have a baby when you are all grown up.

Life is a cycle that we all go through. Puppies grow up into dogs, kittens grow up into cats and children grow up into adults.

What makes puberty happen?

Your body makes special chemicals called hormones. They make your body begin to change.

The hormones are what make puberty happen. Hormones are chemicals that are made in different places throughout our bodies. Hormones travel through our bloodstream from the places that they are made, to other places where they make the changes.

The sex hormones are the hormones that make changes to the sex organs. For males, their testicles will make the hormone testosterone and sperm. For females, their ovaries will start producing progesterone and oestrogen, which then cause the egg (ovum or ova) to be released, breasts to grow, and periods to start. Other changes also start to happen throughout the body, like growing taller, pubic hair, etc.

How do the hormones get started?

When your body has grown to the right size and shape, it will trigger your brain to start sending messages to a small gland at the base of your brain called the pituitary gland, telling it to release growth hormones into your blood stream. The pituitary gland is 'the boss' hormone because it tells all the other glands what they need to do to make puberty happen.

In males, the pituitary gland will tell your testicles to start producing sperm and the hormone testosterone.

In females, the pituitary gland will tell your ovaries to produce progesterone and oestrogen, which then causes the ova (eggs) to be released.

How the body knows to start puberty

Your body just knows, as it is programmed to start when it is ready.

You will start growing and when your body is the right shape and size, your hormone body clock will start ticking. Which means that your body will start producing the sex hormones, which will make your body start to change.

Female bodies can start growing from the ages of 8-9 and male bodies usually start growing from around 11-12.

When will puberty happen?

Everybody is different. For most kids, it can be from as young as 8 or as late as 16.

Your body will start to change when it is the right size and shape for you.

Female bodies go through puberty first. Male bodies usually start 2 years later.

How long will puberty last?

It is different for everyone, but it can be anytime between the ages of 8 and 18. It usually lasts for 4-5 years.

What happens when puberty is finished?
Nothing, you have now fully grown, i.e., an adult.

When will I start growing?
When your body is the right shape and size, your hormone body clock will start ticking. Which means that your body will start producing the sex hormones, which will make your body start to change.

Female bodies can start growing from the ages of 8-9 and male bodies usually start growing from around 11-12.

When will I stop growing?
Female bodies stop growing at around 16 years of age, and male bodies at around 18.

Why is my body so different to my friends?
Everyone is different, which means that we all have different bodies. Some of us have blue eyes and some have brown eyes. Some of us have large breasts and some have small breasts. Either way, your body is special just the way it is.

Puberty starts when your body is ready for it to start.

Why do some kids get embarrassed about puberty?
There are lots of reasons. Sometimes it can take a little bit of time to get used to, especially when other people can see the changes happening too. It can be pretty embarrassing for them when other people make comments about their new and different body.

They might be disappointed or sad that their childhood is finishing. Or scared about what it means to be an adult.

Lots of kids feel embarrassed at some time during puberty.

Why do we have to grow up?
It is something that just happens. You've already grown from being a helpless baby to a child who can do so much. Being an adult is just the next stage, and it has to happen so that you can reproduce and one day maybe have babies of your own.

Why do female bodies go through puberty first?
They start puberty earlier because the pituitary gland is switched on earlier in female bodies than it is in male bodies.

How do I know when puberty is going to happen?
You won't really know until you start to see some changes in your own body. Everyone starts puberty at a different time. Some of your friends will start earlier, later or at the same time as you.

Why do your hormones go crazy during puberty?
The amount of hormones in your body can go up and down each day, which means that your emotions and feelings can go up and down too. Hormones make your body change physically but they also affect how you feel about your body and other people.

Some days you may have high amounts and then other days you may have small amounts. This can sometimes make you feel very different each day.

Hair in funny places

What is pubic hair?

Pubic hair is hair that grows on a vulva or around the penis and on the scrotum.

It starts to grow during puberty.

When will I get pubic hair?

You'll get pubic hair anytime between the ages of 8 to 18. Everyone is different.

Most kids start to notice it from between 11-14 years old.

Why is my pubic hair changing and getting curly?

That is perfectly normal and is just something that happens as you get more and more pubic hair.

Is pubic hair straight or curly?

Pubic hair can be straight or curly and it depends on your cultural background. It can also feel a bit coarser (or rougher) than the hair on your head.

The type of pubic hair that you have is inherited from your family.

Is your pubic hair the same color as the hair on your head?

It usually is, but not always.

Blonde people usually have darker pubic hair.

Your pubic hair will change as you go through puberty. It'll become curlier, thicker and may even change color.

What about armpit hair?

Hair will also grow in your armpit.

It might grow before or after you start growing pubic hair.

Some people like to remove this hair.

Male bodies

What changes happen to male bodies?

- body shape becomes taller, heavier and more muscular, shoulders and chest broaden
- their voice begins to deepen
- armpit and pubic hair begin to grow
- body odor becomes stronger
- erections start happening more frequently (sometimes when you least expect them) and wet dreams occur more frequently
- penis, testicles and scrotum start to grow larger

Why do I have breasts (or man-boobs)?

When puberty first starts, it is quite common for some male bodies to have some swelling around their nipples, from the surge in hormones. It doesn't mean that they will be growing breasts. This swelling will settle down once their shoulders broaden and their muscles start to develop.

It can take a few years for this to settle but don't worry, it is happening to other kids too.

Some people can also feel tender behind the nipple area. This will eventually go away as the hormone levels change.

When will I grow a beard?

Everyone is different, but usually sometime between the ages of 14 to 18. Facial hair is usually one of the last changes from puberty.

When facial hair first starts to grow it usually looks like fluffy hair above the top lip and on your chin.

How much hair you get depends on what the other males in your family have too.

Why does my voice sound different at times?

During puberty, your voice box (the larynx) is getting bigger. Because this growth happens very quickly, it can be hard for people to control the pitch of their voice, especially if they are nervous. Their voice might sound squeaky or go up and down quickly.

This can be very embarrassing for most people.

When will I get pubic hair?

You'll get pubic hair anytime between the ages of 8 to 18. Everyone is different.

Why is my pubic hair changing and getting curly?

That is perfectly normal and is just something that happens as you get more and more pubic hair.

How hairy will I get?

That depends, as it is different for everyone. Some cultural backgrounds have more hair than others.

There are ways to get rid of body hair if you don't want it, but we can talk about that when it happens.

Can males have periods?

Some children will have female reproductive organs but identify as a boy (and not a girl). They will have periods unless they begin transitioning to become a trans man.

Only if they have a uterus, because you need a uterus for periods to happen.

Penises, erections and wet dreams

What is an erection?

An erection is when the amount of blood going to the penis increases, making the penis hard and erect.

An erect penis is much bigger than a soft one and stands away from the body.

All males have erections, but during puberty, they happen more often.

Sometimes erections happen for no reason at all. You don't have to be sexually aroused to have an erection.

Why do I have erections?

All people with penises have erections, and even little kids and babies get them too.

They can happen when you are having sexy thoughts, or when the penis is touched or rubbed by clothing. Sometimes they can happen for no reason at all.

Can I stop myself from having an erection?

During puberty, erections can sometimes happen for no reason at all. It can be very embarrassing for males when this happens.

Unwanted erections will go away more quickly if you think of something else (like saying the alphabet backwards).

Unwanted erections won't happen forever. Once puberty is over, you will find that you have more control over your erections.

Why do I wake up with an erection?

It is common for people to wake up with an erection. They usually happen during the REM (Rapid Eye Movement) phase of sleep, which is just before you wake up. Sometimes it can also be because you have a full bladder.

If you happen to have a sexy dream during this phase, you will sometimes ejaculate.

A full bladder can place pressure on the erectile tissue at the base of the penis, causing an erection. Because you can't wee with an erection, you will have to wait a few minutes for your penis to relax before you can pass urine.

How many erections a day is normal?

It is different for everyone and it depends on what your hormones are doing, too!

You usually get erections because of sexual thoughts and feelings but, during puberty, people can get lots of spontaneous erections, i.e., erections that happen for no apparent reason at all. This can happen to all males.

What is sperm?

Sperm are the male sex cells, i.e., the male part that you need to join with the female ovum (or egg) to make a baby.

Sperm is made in the testicles. They take about 2 weeks to be fully grown and are then stored in the epididymis, where they are either ejaculated out or absorbed back into the body, 4-5 weeks later.

What is semen?

Semen is the liquid that carries the sperm.

Semen is sticky, cloudy (not clear) and whitish in color.

Its job is to keep the sperm healthy.

What's the difference between sperm and semen?

Sperm is made by your testicles during puberty and is needed to make a baby. Semen is the whitish fluid that carries the sperm.

Do I have sperm?

Most male bodies will one day make sperm when they go through puberty, usually when they are between 12-14 years old.

When will I start to make sperm?

People usually start to make sperm when they are 13 and a half. Some will make it sooner and some will make it later.

What does ejaculation mean?

Ejaculation is when semen and sperm come out of the penis.

The fluid comes out in little spurts, anywhere between a teaspoon to a tablespoon in volume.

What does semen look like?

Semen is a whitish fluid. It carries and nourishes the sperm.

Semen is made as the person is ejaculating. The ejaculated sperm are pushed through the ejaculatory duct and fluid from the different glands (seminal vesicles, prostate, and Cowper's gland) are added along the way. Most of the fluid comes from the seminal vesicles and prostate gland.

A typical ejaculate is between a teaspoon and tablespoon of fluid containing at least 30 million sperm.

How old do you have to be to make sperm?
Somewhere between 12 to 14 years of age. It is different for everyone, but it is usually after your penis and scrotum have started to grow.

How does sperm come out?
Semen joins the sperm, and this liquid is pushed out through the penis during muscular contractions, i.e., orgasm. This can happen during masturbation, a wet dream or during sexual intercourse.

Will I run out of sperm?
No, your body makes sperm throughout your whole life.

My penis is growing longer. Is that normal?
Yes, they do that during puberty. They grow longer and then they grow wider.

Why is one of my testicles bigger than the other?
Sometimes this is just what happens. Testicles are often different in size and one may hang a little lower than the other one. This also stops them from knocking against each other.

Is it normal for my penis to bend?
Sometimes the penis can have a slight bend to it, especially when it is erect.

What happens if your foreskin can't push back?
When the penis is erect, the foreskin will automatically pull back by itself. Sometimes you might need to help push it back, to have it pulled back all the way.

If the foreskin is too tight to push back, or if it hurts or is uncomfortable when it is pushed back, you will need to see a Doctor. This is not uncommon and happens to other boys too.

Why does my penis sometimes go small?
Usually, because you are cold. All penises do this.

When people get very cold, their penis and scrotum will shrink up, to keep the penis and testicles warm.

What's a 'wet dream'?
A wet dream is when you ejaculate semen and sperm during your sleep. You might wake up when it happens, or you may just find a wet patch on your pants or sheets the next morning.

Wet dreams only happen once your body starts to make semen and sperm.

This is a normal thing to happen to male bodies. Some people have many; some people, not as many; and some people never have a wet dream.

When will I start to have wet dreams?
Wet dreams only happen once your body starts to make semen and sperm.

Does everyone have set dreams?
No, some people never have wet dreams.

Why do you have wet dreams?

Wet dreams help your body to get rid of the extra sperm that you produce.

It is common for people to experience an erection during the REM (Rapid Eye Movement) phase of sleep, which is the phase just before you wake up. If you happen to have a sexy dream during this phase, you will sometimes ejaculate.

When do wet dreams happen?

Wet dreams happen at nighttime, during your sleep.

How often will I have wet dreams?

Everyone is different. Some kids have lots, some only have one or two, and some kids don't have them at all.

Will I know if I have a wet dream?

Sometimes you might wake up during a wet dream but sometimes you don't know until you wake up with a wet patch on your sheets or pyjamas.

What do I do if I have a wet dream?

You need to decide what you want to happen in your house! Some kids are shyer than others, so it may help to try and work out what they want to do.

That's up to you. What do you think we should do?

You might want to put your pyjamas in the wash basket, or start doing your own washing, or...

Female bodies

What changes happen to female bodies?

- breasts begin to grow and develop
- hips become wider
- thighs and bottoms become more rounded
- armpit and pubic hair begin to grow
- body odour becomes stronger
- uterus, vagina and ovaries grow and begin to release eggs
- menstruation (periods) starts

Why do you get fat at puberty?

You don't necessarily get fatter, but your body will change in anticipation of one day having a baby. Your hips will get wider, which means that there is room for the uterus to grow during pregnancy.

Do some people never get their periods?

Some females don't get their period, but that isn't very common. If they don't have their period by the time they are 16, they usually go and see a doctor about this.

When will my breasts stop growing?

They will usually stop growing by the end of puberty, when you are around 18.

Because breasts are made of fatty tissue, they can grow larger if you increase your body weight.

Why is one of my breasts bigger than the other?

Sometimes this is just what happens. They usually catch up with each other by the time you have finished growing. Most people don't have perfectly matched breasts.

This is happening to other kids too, but no one else will notice but you!

Why is my body so different to my friends?

Everyone is different, which means that we all have different bodies. Some of us have blue eyes and some have brown eyes. Some of us have large breasts and some have small breasts. Either way, your body is special just the way it is.

When will I start growing?

When your body is the right shape and size, your hormone body clock will start ticking. Which means that your body will start producing sex hormones, which will make your body start to change.

Female bodies can start growing from the ages of 8-9 and male bodies usually start growing from around 11-12.

When will I stop growing?

Females stop growing at around 16 years of age, and males at around 18.

Can males have periods?

Some children will have female reproductive organs but identify as a boy (and not a girl). They will have periods until they begin transitioning to become a trans man.

Only if they have a uterus, because you need a uterus for periods to happen.

Why do I get white stuff on my underpants?

That is something that happens to your body as you start puberty. We call it vaginal discharge and it is the vagina's way of cleaning itself.

Why do I sometimes feel wet in my vagina/vulva area?

That is a slippery liquid called mucous. It is supposed to be there, and it keeps your vagina and cervix moist.

Your mucous will change in colour and texture because of the hormones during your menstrual cycle. When an egg is released from the ovary, the mucous is usually slippery and clear like egg white, which helps the sperm to travel more quickly to the egg. At other times of the month, it can be whiter, and even yellowish too.

How big will my vulva grow?

Just like we have different sized feet, we can have differently sized and shaped vulvas. They come in all different sizes, shapes and colours, but you usually end up with the right size vulva for your body.

What's menopause?
Menopause is when your body stops being fertile. It means that you can no longer naturally conceive and grow a baby.

The ovaries will stop releasing eggs and uterus will stop making the thick lining that is needed to receive the fertilised eggs.

What's ovulation?
Ovulation is when the ovary releases a mature egg into the fallopian tubes, ready to be fertilised.

Do you feel the egg being released?
Not usually, but some people do. They might feel a twinge in their tummy area that doesn't last long.

Periods

What's a period?
A period is a small amount of blood that comes out of a person's vagina every month.

Each month, the body prepares itself in case a baby is made. The uterus makes a special lining which is ready for the fertilised egg to land on, which is where it will then grow into a baby. If a baby doesn't happen, the lining is no longer needed. The lining then comes out through the vagina as menstrual blood or a period. Your body will do this each month.

This cycle will keep on happening until your hormones tell it to stop.

What's the menstrual cycle?

The amount of time between the first day of your period and the day before your next period starts. So, if someone got their period on January 1 and then again on January 29, their cycle will have lasted 28 days.

The menstrual cycle is the changes that your body goes through every month to prepare for pregnancy.

When you first start your periods, your cycle can be anywhere between 21-45 days. After a few years, it will decrease to 21-36 days. Everyone is different.

How many days do you bleed for?

A period usually lasts between 3 to 7 days, and it usually happens each month.

Only a small amount of blood comes out – about a third of a cup.

Why do female bodies have periods?

It is a part of the what the body does, to get ready for falling pregnant. Each month the uterus makes a special lining of blood to grow a baby onto. When a baby isn't made, the special lining isn't needed, so it comes out of the vagina as blood.

When do you stop getting your period?

Your period can stop if you are pregnant. It can also stop because of stress, illness, changes in your body weight and even a change in routine, like going on holiday!

Eventually your period will stop when you are about 50 and reach menopause.

Menopause is when your body stops being fertile. It means that you can no longer naturally conceive and grow a baby.

How will you know when you get your period?

You will feel some wetness around your vagina and find a small amount of blood on your undies or when you wipe after going to the toilet.

The blood will change colour from day to day, from pink to red to brown.

Some people get moody around the time of their period.

How often will I get my period?

Periods happen every 3 to 6 weeks.

The average time is 28 days, but it can vary from between 21-36 days. The timing of your period can be affected by things like stress, illness, changes in your body weight and even a change in routine, like going on holiday!

During puberty, periods are not very regular and the average length of time that they last is between 2-8 days.

When will I get my period?
Some kids can be as young as 8 or as old as 16 before they start their period.

Can you get your period when you are pregnant?
No, you can't. Your body will know that it is pregnant and that the lining of the uterus is needed.

Do you sometimes wake up in puddles of blood, when you have your period?
You won't wake up in a puddle of blood, but you might leak blood during the night, staining your pyjamas and/or sheets.

You can use a heavier pad during the night, that will hold more blood.

Does it hurt when you have your period?
Some people might get a twinge in the pelvic area, but most people keep on doing whatever they are normally doing.

Some people can get cramping in the pelvic area or a lower back ache that gets better after a day or two. Some people take pain relief or use a hot pack to help relax the muscles in the pelvic area or lower back.

Eventually your period becomes more regular and predictable once puberty has finished.

How can I keep track of when my period is due?

You can track of when it started in a diary or even download an app to your phone/tablet. This way you can try to work out what your pattern is, and you will have a good idea of when your period is likely to arrive.

When will my periods become regular?

It can take between 2 to 3 years for your periods to become regular.

How much blood do you lose during your period?

About a third to one-half of a cup of blood. It might seem like a lot more than that!

Everyone is different. Some lose more blood, or less blood, than others.

Why do I get cramps during my period?

Your uterus contracts (tightens and relaxes). This helps to remove the lining from the walls of your uterus, which then comes our as menstrual blood.

Some people get more cramping than others.

Can you swim when you have your period?

You can but you will need to use a tampon, a menstrual cup or swimpants. You can't swim with a pad because it will swell up from the water, may even start to fall apart and it will be pretty easy for everyone to know that you are wearing a pad. If you swim without a tampon, the blood will be diluted but it will still run down your leg, which means that people will see it. So, most people choose to not go swimming when they have their period (unless they are using tampons).

What's PMS?

Some people experience a range of different emotional and physical symptoms for a week or so before they get their period, and sometimes even during their period.

Symptoms can include: cramps, backaches, breast tenderness, skin problems, bloating, mild depression, headaches, and/or angry outbursts.

Everyone is different so you may or may not get some of these symptoms. Plus, there are things that we can do to help make you feel better, if you do get any of them.

What do you need for a period?

When you first start, you will probably be using pads. They have a sticky strip and will stick to the inside of your underpants.

When you are a little bit older, you can look at using tampons. They are inserted into your vagina and absorb the blood inside there.

Pads

What are pads?

A pad is something that you use to absorb blood when you have your period. You wear it in your underpants, and it sits between your legs, touching your vulva.

It has a sticky strip that helps it to attach to your underpants and to stay in place.

Why do some pads have wings?

Some pads do have wings. They wrap around the crotch of your underpants and can help to stop the blood from going onto them. Some wings have an absorbent material and will stop the pad from leaking in the middle.

How often do you need to change your pad?

When the pad looks full towards the centre, it is usually a good time to change it. Every 3-4 hours is a good frequency, which means during recess and lunch breaks whilst at school. You can sleep in the one pad at night, and just change it when you wake up.

If the pad feels wet or soggy, it means that it needs to be changed.

Pads can start to smell after about 5-6 hours, especially on a hot and sweaty day.

How long do pads last?

A pad will last anywhere between 2 to 7 hours, depending on your blood flow. If you are bleeding more heavily, the pad won't last as long.

Why are there so many different types of pads?

It can get pretty confusing when you look at all the different types of pads. Basically, some are just longer or shorter, wider or narrower, thicker or thinner, heavier or lighter. The companies that make them have come up with lots of different fancy names.

What are panty liners for?

Panty liners are a much smaller, thinner pad that will hold a small amount of blood or vaginal discharge.

Can I flush pads down the toilet?

No, there is a good chance that it will block the toilet. If there isn't a bin in the toilet cubicle, you can wrap the pad up into the packet that the new pad came out of (or in lots of toilet paper) and place it in the bin next to the hand basin.

Some kids have a special period kit that they take to the toilet with them. You can keep plastics bags in there that are for holding used pads and tampons. You can use this to hold any used pads, then just throw them away when you get home.

Tampons

What is a tampon?

A tampon is something that you insert into your vagina to catch the blood before it comes out. It is a finger-shaped wad of absorbent material, just like what is in pads.

Vaginas are very stretchy and have no trouble holding a tampon.

Do I have to use tampons?

No, only if you want to. Most kids start off with using pads and then start using tampons because they want to play sport whilst they have their period.

Everyone is different. Some people don't use tampons, some people use both tampons and pads, and some people only use tampons.

How do I put a tampon in?

Some kids are fine with using tampons, but some are more nervous. If they can insert a finger fully into their vagina, they should be fine with inserting a tampon. Sometimes it can help if they use a dab of vaginal lubricant on the tip of the tampon. This helps the tampon to glide in rather than drag in. You can also buy small tampons or tampons that are covered in a silky covering that make insertion much easier.

They aren't that hard to put in. Inside the tampon packet, you will find some instructions on how to insert them. First, you find a position that is comfortable. You can squat, sit down on the toilet or stand with leg up on the toilet. You take the tampon out of its wrapper, part the opening to your vagina, and push the tampon up into your vagina.

We can talk about this more when you are ready to start using tampons.

Do tampons hurt when you insert them?

Some kids may want to practice inserting a tampon before they have their next period. This will be uncomfortable and difficult to do. So, make sure that they know that they know that they need to actually be bleeding, and the heavier their flow, the easier it will be to insert that first tampon.

If you try to insert a tampon into a vagina that isn't bleeding, it will be uncomfortable.

It won't hurt but it can be uncomfortable. If you can relax, it makes the muscles around the vagina will soften and loosen, which means that it will be easier to push the tampon in. You do have to make sure though that you are bleeding at the time.

Sometimes you can put a dab of lubricant on the end of the tampon to make it easier for it to go in. This has to be proper vaginal lubricant and should be freshly opened (not opened up years ago).

Do tampons hurt when you wear them and move around?

If you put it in properly, meaning it is far enough into the vagina, it won't be uncomfortable. You don't feel a properly inserted tampon. If it isn't pushed in far enough, it will feel uncomfortable.

Don't worry about the tampon going in too far and getting lost. The cervix at the end of the vagina will stop it from going any further than it should. The string is there so that you can pull the tampon out.

Some brands of tampon are easier to use than others. So, it is a good idea to buy a few different brands, for your first time.

Why are there 2 types of tampons?

You can buy tampons with an applicator or without an applicator. The longer one is a normal-sized tampon that comes with an applicator, which helps to push the tampon up into the vagina. The shorter ones don't have an applicator, which means that you need to use your clean finger to push the tampon up into the vagina.

Each person is different and uses the type of tampon that they are comfortable with. Some people don't use tampons at all.

Which type of tampon should I start with?

It all depends on how old you are and how comfortable you are with putting your fingers into your vagina. Some people like to use applicators, and some don't. Sometimes it can be easier with an applicator. Make sure you start off with the smallest size (lightest) tampon that you can find.

How do I know where to put the tampon?

Some kids are totally ignorant of what they have between their legs. So, they may need some encouragement to go and grab a mirror and to have a look at what they actually have between their legs.

The tampon goes into the vagina, the middle opening. There is only one opening that is big enough for a tampon. It is the one that you can feel if you have a little feel in your vulva area.

How long do I leave the tampon in for?

It all depends on how heavy your blood flow is, but it could need changing as often as every 2-6 hours. Your confidence with using tampons will increase, as you start using them.

It is harder to tell when a tampon is full, as the blood is all inside. When it is getting full, the tampon string will be stained with blood and blood will leak onto your underpants. Some people like to wear a small pad or panty liner until they are more confident with using tampons.

Can I use a tampon overnight?

You shouldn't use a tampon overnight as they need to be changed every 6-8 hours. Plus, it could be unsafe because of Toxic Shock Syndrome (TSS).

Toxic Shock Syndrome (TSS) is a rare bacterial infection that is linked to the use of tampons. It is rare but can kill women.

How do I get the tampon out?

There is a string at the end of the tampon that stays outside the vagina when you insert it. When you tug at the string, the tampon will slide out.

Can a tampon fall out?

No, once it is in the vagina, it will stay there. If you haven't pushed it up far enough into the vagina, it might feel uncomfortable, though.

What happens if a tampon gets stuck up there?

It is pretty uncommon for a tampon to get stuck. Sometimes, though, they can be a bit tricky to remove, usually because there is not enough moisture in them.

If one does get stuck, you can try squatting down and relaxing the vaginal muscles as you pull down. You can also try putting clean fingers into the vagina to help pull the tampon out. If it gets too stressful, stop for half an hour and then go back and try again.

If it does get stuck, you can ring your local Women's Health Centre, STI Clinic or doctor for it to be removed. Make sure you tell them when you call so that you get an appointment that day.

Can I flush tampons down the toilet?

No, there is a good chance that it will block the toilet. If there isn't a bin in the toilet cubicle, you can wrap the tampon up in lots of paper and place it in the bins next to the hand basin.

Some kids have a special period kit that they take to the toilet with them. You can keep plastics bags in there that are for holding used pads and tampons. You can use this to hold any used tampons, then just throw them away when you get home.

Can you still go to the toilet if you have a tampon in?

Yes, you can. Your urine will just run out as it normally does. You may want to lift the tampon string out of the way though, so that it doesn't get wet!

Are tampons dangerous?

Tampons aren't dangerous if they are used properly. You need to have clean hands, and not leave them in the vagina for too long. Tampons have been linked with a rare but serious infection called Toxic Shock Syndrome (TSS).

Sexual intercourse

When talking to kids about sex, you can add a value statement about the situations in which you believe sex should happen, e.g. 'In our family, we believe that you shouldn't have sex until...' (you are married, in a loving and committed relationship, are 16, or whatever it is that you believe in).

What is sex?

Sex can be lots of different things, but usually when you hear people talking about sex, they are talking about sexual intercourse, i.e., penis-in-vagina sex.

What is sexual intercourse?

When two adults like each other a lot, they may want to have sexual intercourse with each other. This means that they may hug, kiss and touch each other's bodies all over. The penis becomes erect and the vagina becomes moist and slippery. This makes it easier for the penis to go into the vagina. The male pushes their penis into the vagina (or the female lets the male push their penis into the vagina), they hold each other close, they move around a bit and it can feel good. After a while, the male almost always ejaculates.

Adults have sexual intercourse because they like the way it feels. Their whole body feels good, not just their genitals.

Sexual intercourse is something very private and should happen with (insert your values).

What is foreplay?

Foreplay is the name for all the other stuff, like cuddling and kissing and touching each other's bodies. The stuff that helps to get you into the mood for sex.

What happens when you have sex?

There are lots of different ways to have sex. The main way that adults have sex to make a baby is when the penis goes into the vagina. They also do other things like hug, kiss, and touch each other's bodies in a nice way.

Sex is something that most people do when they are grown up.

Will I ever want to hug and kiss someone?

You probably will one day. During puberty, you may start to think about sex differently. This is because of your hormones.

You might find that you start thinking about someone in a new way. You may think about them a lot, have butterflies in your stomach when you meet & daydream about holding hands with them, hugging and kissing.

Will I have sex one day?

Yes, you probably will have sex one day, but it won't be until you are an adult.

When will I want to have sex?

You won't be interested in having sex until puberty happens. Once your body starts making hormones, you will start to think about sex and about people in a different way.

Most people don't just have sex with a complete stranger. They usually start off by getting to know another person first, then become friends. The couple will usually hold hands, hug, cuddle and kiss before they get to the sex part.

Where do adults have sex?

Usually somewhere private, like in their bedroom.

Why do people have sex?

Adults have sex for lots of different reasons. To make babies, to show their love for each other, for fun, because it feels good, or to make you feel closer to each other. Having sex is a natural, normal and healthy part of life.

Having sex with someone can be a very intimate experience to share. You can connect with your partner at the most intimate and knowing level that there is.

A lot of things usually happen before a relationship becomes sexual. The two people usually start off being friends first and will hold hands, hug, cuddle and kiss before they get to the sex part.

Do you have to lie down to have sex?
If you want to, you can. There are lots of different ways that adults can position their bodies to have sexual intercourse.

How old do you have to be to have sex?
The law says that you have to be (the legal age where you live). But in our family, we think that you shouldn't have sex until (insert your values).

How do two women have sex?
There is more to sex than penises and vaginas. It is also about kissing, hugging, and touching each other's genitals. Gay (or lesbian) women can do all of this except for putting a penis in a vagina.

How do two men have sex?
There is more to sex than penises & vaginas. It is also about kissing, hugging, & touching each other's genitals. Gay men can do all of this

except for putting a penis in a vagina. They may have anal intercourse instead.

What is an orgasm?

An orgasm is a really nice feeling that you can get during sex or when you touch your genitals in a nice way (masturbate). For males, it usually happens when the semen comes out of the man's penis. For females, it can happen when the outside of the vulva and/or clitoris is rubbed or during vaginal penetration.

How do you have an orgasm?

Orgasms can happen during sexual activity, masturbation and during a wet dream. They don't just happen randomly. They happen because of sexual pleasure.

You can access my FREE sex education course for parents at https://sexedrescue.com/back-to-basics/

CONCLUSION

Congratulations! The fact that you have bought (and hopefully read) this book, means that your child is fortunate! They are fortunate because they have a parent who:

- Wants to support them as they go through a major phase of change in their life.
- Is someone they can turn to for the support, guidance and information that they need, instead of turning to their friends or the internet.
- Wants to make sure that they have a better experience of puberty than the one they had.
- Wants to talk openly with them about love, sex and relationships, even though sometimes it would be a lot easier to just avoid the topic.
- Is prepared to guide them as they work out what sexual behaviors and attitudes are right for them, instead of leaving them to work it out on their own.
- Is now well prepared to start talking to them about puberty and sex, after reading this book.

So, keep this book as a resource that you can turn to when you need it. It will let you know the why, what, when and how of talking to your child about puberty.

And remember, it isn't so much *what* you say that matters, it is that you're talking to your child about growing up, and by talking, your relationship with them will grow stronger as they blossom into a beautiful young adult.

Enjoy the journey!

RESOURCES

If you are looking for a list of resources on puberty, then you won't find that in this book.

Why? Because by the time you have gotten around to reading this book, the list will already be out of date!

So instead of providing you with a list that is already out of date, I'll tell you about some online resources that I update regularly whenever I find some new content, discover a new website, read a new journal article or blogpost, or buy a newly published book.

So...

- To get started with sex education, sign up for my FREE sex education course for parents: https://sexedrescue.com/back-to-basics/
- To find a list of all the wonderful content that is available on the internet on puberty, you can go to: https://sexedrescue.com/sex-education-resources/

- To find a comprehensive list of puberty books for your child to read, you can go to: https://sexedrescue.com/sex-education-books-for-children/
- To ask questions about sex education and to connect with other parents on the same journey, you can join my free parent Facebook group: https://www.facebook.com/groups/thatparentgroup/
- To receive regular information about sex education, you can sign up for my newsletter: https://sexedrescue.com/newsletter/
- Plus, you will find videos, articles and lots of other educational content at Sex Ed Rescue: https://sexedrescue.com

ABOUT THE AUTHOR

Cath Hakanson has been talking to clients about sex for the past 25 years as a nurse, midwife, sex therapist, researcher, blogger and educator. She's spent the past 10 years trying to unravel why parents (herself included) struggle with sex education. Her solution was to create Sex Ed Rescue, an online resource that simplifies sex education and helps parents to empower their children with the right information about sex, so kids can talk to them about anything, no matter what.

Cath has lived all over Australia but currently lives in Perth with her partner, 2 children, and ever-growing menagerie of pets. Despite having an unusual profession, she bakes, sews, and knits for sanity, collects sexual trivia, and tries really hard not to embarrass her children in public. Well, most of the time anyway!

If you'd like to know more, please visit my online home at SexEdRescue.com